The Return of Little Jack
Spits, Hisses & Furbaby Kisses
by
Davina Hanes
ISBN; 978-1-9997646-5-4

Published by

i2i Publishing.
Manchester M25 0NL UK
www.i2ipublishing.co.uk

All Royalties from this book will go to Oldham Cats
Rescue

Charity number: 1058621

*To Knuspy
love Little Jack xxx*

Dedication

I dedicate this book to three exceptional angels who have been an incredible inspiration to me in my life and indeed to many others who have been fortunate enough to know them.

Jill Murfin, you are an exceptional angel with an immense heart. Your special love, care and dedication towards Little Jack throughout has touched many. Little Jack has gained a true angel; me, a wonderful friend. You're an incredible part of Little Jack's life and the love you've so humbly poured into this boy will never be forgotten.

Lucy Cobb, a second angel and a very dear friend. I'm overcome by your love, kindness and your enormous heart. Animals have a unique gift; that gift being their amazing ability to bring people together. Your following of Little Jack and indeed love for him has developed into a special life-long friendship. I thank you for being the graceful angel you are.

Sylvia Barry, a treasured friend, a beautiful angel, you have left paw prints on our hearts. You are sadly missed but your legacy lives on through Oldham Cats. As your spirit surrounds us, you'll always be cherished and never forgotten.

I'm honoured to have, and have had, such amazing and inspirational angels in my life.

The return of Little Jack
'Spits, Hisses and Furbaby Kisses'

An Evolving World

A life that was destined to curdle into loneliness and disappointment, I lowered my head in pain and despairingly I scrambled on, my entire world enveloped in darkness.
In desperation, I used my sharp senses and whiskers to help me along my lonely nomadic journey through the streets.
Cold and so hungry, I fearfully cowered along the edge of the pavement, bristling my tail at the unfamiliar noises that surrounded me. A bitter, damp February day it was as I scrambled on, my tiny ginger frame often camouflaged to those around me, amongst debris and litter.

Why? Why me?

Sadly, I'd become accustomed to the uncaring footsteps that frequently passed by. An ignoring and uncaring world I thought despairingly as I manoeuvred my tiny body clumsily along the pavement in search of food, in search of hope.

The haunting feelings all came crashing down upon me; fear, loneliness, pain, impending doom, desperation. Startled and bewildered, I raised my head as momentarily that fear and loneliness gripped me once again, as it did frequently. One could never forget. Suddenly realisation dawned. It was only a dream, a distant memory from my past...

One year on, it seemed like a lifetime ago when, at eighteen weeks of age, I wandered the streets of Manchester as an abandoned blind kitten. Yet months later, the fear and desperation were still etched in my memory, still so vivid.

I snuggled deeper into the crook of my human Mummy Davina's arm, enjoying the aesthetically pleasing warmth, security and love my family now provided me.

It was night time, of this I knew but not because of the pitch blackness. Darkness had become my world all that time ago on the precarious streets during my ordeal.

I established it was night-time simply due to my Daddy's nearby snoring and the unusual silence within the household. A household constantly full of play, frolics, mischief, pattering paws, meows and purrs with my fellow furry feline friends, all twelve of them.

Boing! The mattress suddenly dipped, the sheer enormity of the suspension almost propelling me into the air.

"Move over Buddy," Mr Magic Hanes spoke in a gruff voice, his belly rumbling as he brushed past me impatiently.

"I don't want to...I'm too comfy," I replied with defiance but knowing I would have to do so soon, in order for Magic to perform his daily ritual.

Mr Magic Hanes was Mummy and Daddy's first Rescue cat from Oldham Cats, a senior chap of almost 20 years of age now, and one whom we all treated with unprecedented respect.

A black cat of larger proportion with a swishing belly he was, a senior chap who enjoyed his lazy days and his romantic rendezvous with his fine lady Candy. Yes, they attempted to mask their romance somewhat; the brood and myself weren't fooled though, not at all.

Candy would purr provocatively near Magic and whenever possible they would spend lazy siestas together, spooned into one another.

I yawned and shuffled down the bed reluctantly in order to allow Mr Magic Hanes access to Mummy's pillow so he could perform his daily enactment of waking mummy.

The pitter-patter of paws slowly approached and the mattress dipped yet again, this time on Daddy's side of the bed.

"Come on Magic," Peanut squeaked impatiently, "we're hungry. Remember, it's Mummy's Rescue day, she'll need to get up soon anyway. Come on Magic, we're bloody starving!"

A slight understatement from Peanut, I mused as he was constantly starving!

The Rescue...it certainly must be Mummy's day at Oldham Cats Rescue, I realised, as her working boots were readily situated in the hallway from the night previous.

Oldham Cats Rescue; my saviour.

It was that very little haven of a Rescue that accepted me as a stray kitten in need of surgery to my eye, the same Rescue with volunteers who never gave up hope with me.

Very soon after my arrival at the Rescue, Crown House Vets operated on me. Sadly, my eye required removal due to its terribly ulcerated and bulbous state. It soon became apparent to the humans in my life that I had, nor still have, any vision in my one remaining, lonesome eye.

Darkness I was certainly accustomed to and it posed no threat within the security and sanctuary of my own home with my adopted family.

My initial integration however with my furry family did indeed present many challenges as did familiarising myself to an alien environment...home.

Mummy and Daddy realised minor changes needed to be made, such as not moving furniture around and not leaving obstacles in my path as the home presented itself as a maze to me at first.

I would recklessly bump into objects, yet within time, I diligently had everything mapped out within the home, barring the odd bump or collision. With a determined mind and with the sharpest of senses, I eventually discovered my way around the home. I had no choice... absolutely anything to persuade Daddy to adopt me. I remember the enormity of the task so very well!

I was taken to the Hanes residence post-surgery for my recuperation period. Mummy, a volunteer at Oldham Cats was more than obliging to help care for me and all volunteers decided a caged environment at the Rescue was certainly unsuitable during my recovery.

I soon discovered I wanted to call this place my home...I desperately wanted to belong.

Mummy Davina fell in love with me instantaneously and was certainly more than accommodating from the onset. Similarly, Baby Holly (my four-legged furry mentor) accepted me within no time and I shadowed her everywhere, absolutely everywhere.

However, my receiving of Daddy's admission of love and agreement to a forever home was slow in forthcoming. This proved a strenuous task indeed to try and convince him.

Fortunately, I soon had Daddy wrapped around my ginger paws as with every given opportunity I would clamber up his legs and settle myself on his knee, purring profusely. His declaration of love came soon enough and gradually within time the brood accepted I had become a permanent new addition to the family...

"Oh, come on, dear!" Candy's indignant purr brought me back to the present as she addressed Magic. And indeed, more prevailing issues... our breakfast!

Tummy rumbling, I shuffled down the bed even further, allowing Magic to fulfil his daily ritual.

The bedroom had suddenly come to life some with the pitter patter of paws, rumbling tummies and copious meows.

With a gentle paw Magic tapped Mummy Davina on the shoulder several times. No response.

"Harder Magic!" Baby Peanut, the 'trouble shooter' began to chant, "Harder!"

Magic needed no more prompting and batted Mummy more swiftly.

Mummy Davina groaned, shifted and covered her head with the duvet in protest.

Magic resumed his relentless quest with determination and precision. He had now positioned himself on the pillow and briskly clipped mummy across her head, he had long since mastered this technique...Not quite causing Mummy extreme pain, but administering enough force to startle her.

"Magic! Stop!" Mummy groaned, her voice groggy from her disturbed sleep. Magic meowed repeatedly, continuing to challenge Mummy until she finally submitted and reluctantly clambered out of bed.

Only Magic Hanes could ever get away with this, only Magic ever dared to.

Mummy had told us the tale many a time of how she first developed a newfound love for our feline kind. She had become a tad smitten with her friends' cat, the beautiful late 'Pancake', a rescue from Oldham Cats. Daddy and herself gave the issue much consideration, in terms of offering a furry a forever home, and within weeks they ventured to the Rescue.

"How did you get them to choose you?" I once asked Magic Hanes curiously.

"Hhhmm…" he pondered, "well it was the 31st January and the rescue was full of colourful felines. Younger and prettier than me, I suppose. I was in the very top last cage. I'd been there for some time, found as a stray I was, and my cage constantly went unnoticed despite my vocal nature. I was so fed up I even escaped the confinement of my cage the day previous…Just desperate to get out." He went quiet for a moment, reminiscing, his face saddened by the memory, his whiskers twitching.

"When Mummy and Daddy arrived", he continued, "I listened as Mummy told the volunteer she wanted something young, possibly colourful. No way! Not again! I thought to myself so I set about working my magic on them." The pride in his voice was unmistakable.

"Well, how did you manage that then?" I prompted.

"I simply meowed and meowed and when at last they arrived at my cage, I rolled over and you know, just did my stuff. "

"What stuff, Magic?" I asked curiously.

"You know, the usual. I purred and dribbled and rolled over…there was no way I was letting them leave without me. A panther like me was certainly far too handsome for a cage. Quite satisfied with myself I was on that day, Little Jack." Magic held his head high proudly, reflecting upon the moment.

"Wow Magic!" I replied, having the upmost respect for this wise old man.

The sound of the shower brought me back to the present.

Daddy had woken by now and was preparing for the day ahead. The scent of Mummy drowned in an abundance of overpowering perfume caused my nostrils to flare and also informed me that she was on task. Yucky stuff, I thought.

Despite the aroma, I was eager to follow the sound of her clanging the empty dishes upstairs and I bounded off the bed, almost crashing into Peanut.

Hurling, bashing, jumping and meowing; a stampede of feline furries joined me as I followed Mummy down the stairs. I had long since mastered these, knowing exactly how many there were; yes, occasionally I had the odd mishap, but more often than not, I was fully competent at running up and down now.

"Come on little ones," Mummy stroked and patted us all individually, her love for us unrelenting.

Peanut curled his body around her feet, rubbing against Mummy's leg with the loudest of purrs.

"C'mon woman...less of the soppy stuff! Get on with breakfast!" he muttered impatiently, his feelings masked with copious meows.

Following Mummy, I trotted towards the kitchen alongside Holly, "If only she knew what you were saying Peanut, she'd be furious." I shook my head in disbelief.

"You'll learn Jack," he defended," This kinda reaction gets you far. Watch!" he enthused with clarity.

True to his word Mummy bent down and stroked Peanut some more.

"Aaaaw, are you giving me cuddles Baby Peanut?" Mummy smiled.

"No, I'm bloody well hungry!" Peanut grunted under his breath.

Of course, his pathetic show of affection resulted in him being first place at the feeding bowl as he nosed and rubbed his way forward.

"See, I told you so." Peanut boasted in between a mouth full of food. "These human slaves are so naïve at times."

"Do they not realise, food is the only thing on our mind at this time in the morning?" Magic stalked the work surface impatiently now, "Disillusioned at times is Mummy...mistaking such shows of affection as our undying love for her. In actual fact, we're just bloody hungry!"

Jasper hovered in the doorway tolerantly, his immense frame cushioning him against the hard flooring. "Mind your language near the young ones Magic," he admonished.

"Um, yeah," Magic was distracted some now as a dish was placed in front of him.

The kitchen was now a hive of activity, water running, dishes clanging, paws pitter-pattering and hungry meows, which dominated above all else.

In the distance, I could hear the sound of Daddy spraying the litter trays, his very undignified and unique role within the home. Pooh! Morning aromas emanating from those trays simply weren't the best pleasure one could experience!

We had all taken our positions in the kitchen whilst Mummy washed the dishes and began to distribute the food; Magic Hanes, Peanut, Little Man Max and Simba the Destroyer had long since mounted the kitchen worktop, whilst Baby Holly and myself circled Mummy's feet, our tummies rumbling.

"Are we hungry, little ones?" Mummy's smile could be heard in her voice as she focused her attention to those on the worktop. Despite the fact that Peanut got 'first-dibs' on this occasion, Magic always got fed first; he was a bit like Resident Toby at the Rescue; delving into the dish straight away, unsatisfied with this even, he would then dip curiously into every other dish.

Well of course we're hungry Mummy, I thought, my own impatience creeping in now.

"Do you think chicken is on the menu this morning Holly?" I whispered, not wanting the remainder of the brood to hear.

"Hhhhmm...possibly Jack. Jack, do that thing again then we can be guaranteed some," she replied, batting her lashes.

Oh my! Holly had me wrapped around her mischievous paws! She knew how Mummy concerned herself so much when I wouldn't eat the mandatory food and Holly knew only too well the succulent chicken would then be a welcome alternative.

I continued to circle Mummy's ankles, my meow more of a chirp these days.

"Hang fire Little Jack, it's coming," she said consolingly, "hang fire!"

I gripped my claws into her boots, ready for my onslaught up her legs.

1,2,3...

"Ouch! Jack! Not again!" a bellow from Mummy.

Within seconds I had clawed my way up her legs, unceremoniously swinging from her jumper. I loved this new trick of mine and the dangling sensation was so much fun as I dug my claws deeper into her clothing, my body swishing and swaying mischievously.

Mummy knelt down and carefully unpicked my claws from her now pulled top.

She stroked my head as I faced her proudly.

"You need to stop doing this little man. It hurts. Here, din-dins," she prompted, placing a bowl of food next to me. My nostrils twitched and tempted by the fishy aroma I eagerly began to devour my breakfast. Food a distraction, I forgot my pledge to Holly until she brushed past me, the waft of her tail clipping me across the head.

"Really Jack, you must learn to control yourself. We can certainly say goodbye to the chicken now. You know how I like the chicken. Friends can fall out you know Little Jack!" She

huffed and reluctantly began to eat from her own bowl, her own hunger giving way to defeat.
Guiltily, I continued to eat mine before Mr Magic Hanes even attempted to approach my portion of food.

Mummy clambered around us with more bowls clinging from her hands as she proceeded to take them upstairs to feed the others. Little Treacle, Candy and Princess Zena often loved to dine from the sanctuary of Mummy and Daddy's bedroom. Spoilt, that's what they were...spoilt! Even I had to show some etiquette and come down stairs with the remainder of the brood at mealtimes. As always though, us felines dictated everything that went on in the Hanes household.

I nudged my bowl away and scraped my paws along the floor, a sure sign that my appetite was momentarily appeased.
The sudden clanging of a cat carrier in the lounge immediately diverted my attention.

"Good morning, baby boy!" Daddy greeted me whilst placing a fleece in the carrier. He turned and collected me in his arms and lovingly I reciprocated the affection with a repetition of purrs.
"Baby Boy!" Teddy Bear Thor scoffed as he sauntered past. "You certainly ain't looking like no baby anymore. You'll have an ass as wide as mine in no time, lad!"

Well, it 'ain't nowhere near that big yet! I thought, wounded by his words. I had a long way to go before reaching his colossal size.
Thor, nicknamed 'Teddy Bear' was indeed a gentle giant, a handsome semi long haired tabby with the most affectionate nature, most of the time that is. Of course, due to my lack of vision his refined looks weren't visible to me but during our

playtime frolics, the enormity of his furry frame could certainly be judged.

So, it was my Mummy's day at the Rescue today I mused. That meant only one thing, another trip for Holly and myself. When there was a cage vacant at the Rescue, Mummy still preferred to take Holly and I, still very overprotective of me.

I had become extremely fond of my Rescue experiences over the months, one would think being confined to a cage for the day would be a depressive experience; not for Holly and myself! Firstly, we knew it would only be for the day and secondly, well, we had each other to entertain ourselves, that was when we weren't being showered with cuddles from supporters who regularly visited the Rescue.

And what incredible supporters and Facebook members of Oldham Cats there were, I reflected, remembering the kindness from these humans. My mummy spoke to me often about them, humbled and so appreciative of their generosity, love and care.

Upon my initial arrival to the Rescue, news had circulated within hours on social media of the surgery I required to my eye. Needless to say, these incredible people funded the cost of the operation.

Several weeks following my arrival at the Hanes', I was victim to a further health relapse; a viral infection and I was subsequently rushed to 'Armac Emergency Vets'.

Immediate intravenous fluids and drugs were administered due to my dehydration, high temperature and lethargy. The 'flu-like' symptoms came on spontaneously and I was subjected to isolation at the vets for two days. A terrifying ordeal but the 'Lion Heart' I am; I fought this episode with vigour. Again, precious members within the Facebook Group stepped up once more to fund my treatment.

One member in particular chose the bulk of this funding as her birthday gift. Lucy, she was called. She had been to choose the special present from her husband and after much contemplation she returned home from Manchester, seeing nothing she liked. She switched on her laptop later that day and my face popped up on her news feed on Facebook. With a heavy heart, she continued to follow my story. Lucy, already a sponsor of Resident Toby and a supporter of Oldham Cats, wanted to extend her generosity and her alternative to a designer handbag was indeed to pay for the majority of my veterinary fees, thus helping myself and indeed the Rescue. What followed was a special friendship between my Mummy and Lucy...but more importantly another friendship for me. Lucy continued to follow my story and indeed visit me.

"Jack, I've certainly met some remarkable angels through you," Mummy said, stroking me one day. "You've certainly got the gift of bringing people together."

Such kindness will always remain close to my heart; thoughtfulness and love, which I'll never forget.

The benevolence and care from the public didn't stop there however; they extended their generosity frequently to so many other little furries who were suffering a crisis at Oldham Cats, and indeed over time, there were many at the Rescue.

From such a lonely existence as a stray kitten living in an uncaring world, I now understood that these humans could love, and furthermore, I now understood how love could feel.

Who would ever have thought that a blind, ugly and flea infested little kitten would ever experience such care and devotion, even from people who he had not even met?

"You have your own little fan club going on with that Facebook Group, buddy," Daddy would often say to me. And that I did.

People would enquire after me with genuine care; I had toys knitted for me from a lady called Beryl, toys posted out to me, cards with kind words inside and people would frequently visit me at the Rescue.

From my sad and very humble beginnings, I actually felt such a special little character now. As much as I couldn't see the world, I certainly felt the love within it from these special humans.

People had raised so much money to support my troublesome journey right from the onset; from the moment I arrived at the Rescue, I was so blessed, yes that is what I was…blessed.

Having no sight didn't affect my love of life nor quality of life whatsoever. On the contrary, in some ways the challenges it presented made life far more interesting at times.

Oldham Cats Rescue

Weekends frequently proved to be interesting, Mummy and Daddy didn't go to that Monday to Friday place called work and the superfluous brood and myself rejoiced in the additional time that was spent with us.

Yes, weekends were certainly fun, in particular the days Mummy visited the Rescue, escorted by Baby Holly and myself, when permissible.

The small haven of a Rescue indeed was the pivotal point in my life, without which, who knows what my destiny would have been?

I dare not ponder too much, reminiscing sometimes hurt; haunting me even.

"Are you taking both Jack and Holly, Davi?"

Daddy's enquiring voice suddenly disturbed my train of thought.

"Yes, I certainly am," Mummy replied and airlifted me into an embrace. "You can come today little fella," she addressed me directly and kissed the top of my head.

Jeepers! I wish she wouldn't perform this hideous act in front of the rest of the brood. This act certainly didn't earn me any street credit. I could feel numerous pairs of supercilious eyes glaring into me.

"You're bloody kidding, right?" mumbled Thor, somewhat peeved. "You get to go again. It's always YOU that goes with Mummy!"

"Now! Now! We'll have none of that," Grandpa Jasper reprimanded, pausing momentarily from washing his paws.

I could feel the whoosh of a breeze pass by as Thor marched through to the hallway disdainfully, Princess Zena Warrior in tow, yet another indivisible duo within the brood.

"I'll collect their things," offered Daddy, "what food do you need? Chicken?"

A spontaneous purr erupted from myself and I nudged my head closer into the crook of Mummy's arm, just to remind her of how much she actually loved me; a premeditated act that would hopefully influence her answer.

"Hhhmm...yes chicken I think," she replied and stroked me before placing me into the carrier. Within minutes she had scooped up Holly who likewise accompanied me.

The journey to the Rescue was becoming a little less comfortable these days due to the confined space in our cat carrier. At one time we could potter around in it, play in it even, now however, we simply barely had enough room to manoeuvre.

"Jack, move your butt!" Holly hissed impatiently.

"You move yours," I replied curtly, "yours is getting a tad big too."

"That's no way to speak to a lady!" she scoffed petulantly.

"Remember I know all your secrets; like when you damage things on purpose and that time when you licked Daddy's tea. Oh! and you never say excuse me when you fart and..."

"... Sshhh! They're talking." Holly interrupted impatiently.

We became silent to listen into Mummy and Daddy's conversation.

"What about writing a book about Little Jack?" Daddy asked.

The car drew to a sudden halt, propelling us both to one side of the carrier. Daddy, as always, was such an impatient driver.

"Do you think so?" Mummy pondered some. "There has been a lot of interest over the Facebook Group. It's whether it would sell. It would be fantastic to raise some money for the Rescue wouldn't it?"

'You can only try," prompted Daddy with encouragement.

"I always dreamt of writing a book when I was a little girl..." Mummy broke off, immersed in thought.

"Wow! That must have been a long time ago," I whispered to Holly.

"Sure, must have been. But did you hear them Little Jack. Mummy is going to write a book all about you!" Holly exclaimed.

"I know," I whispered, somewhat overwhelmed, "but Holly, what is there to write about, I'm not exciting or interesting. Just look at me Holly, I can't even see. I must look so grotesque with no eye. No one would be interested in reading about me, an unwanted stray. I can't do half the things you guys do. Not interesting at all." I murmured, feeling deflated.

Holly nestled into me and nudged my lowered head, "Oh Jack! Don't ever think like that. You're handsome and brave and amazing. You're a 'Lion Heart' Little Jack...So clever too. We are actually proud of you; you are so courageous. You have learned so much already. You really have. Deep down the brood really admire you, you know. You must realise that. You may not be able to climb great heights but just look how you have mastered so much in such a short space of time. You're incredible." Holly encouraged.

"You really think so?"

"Jack, I know so." Holly purred.

After much preamble, the car drew to a halt and the jingle of Mummy's gate keys informed me we had arrived at the Rescue.

The morning passed quickly, Holly and I knew the drill only too well. The overwhelming scent of other furries and the multitude of meows and purrs that permeated the room informed me we had indeed entered the 'Adult Room'... a room that was always full of abandoned cats awaiting their forever homes.

They arrived from diverse circumstances; some mistreated, some abandoned and others arrived due to sad circumstances that life inflicted such as bereavement, marital break-ups and even eviction.

Mummy always spoke about the felines awaiting their forever homes, some cases were certainly more heart wrenching than others. All of the stories saddened me, reminding me of my lonely existence on the streets of Manchester. I recalled how at that point in my life, no one cared other than the one woman who discovered me on those very streets and took me to Oldham Cats Rescue.

The Rescue was indeed a small haven, run by unpaid volunteers; dedicated individuals who sacrificed so much time to care for our feline kind.

The successful running of the Rescue was down to an incredible team of devoted individuals, all driven by the same level of love and dedication for the furies. All Angels.

It wasn't a glamorous job, not by any means, and it was one which involved hard labour. There were of course sad moments, moments when those who didn't make it due to illness passed over Rainbow Bridge. The good moments far outweighed anything though; moments when felines would be rehomed and moments when they would overcome illness.

Without the exceptional support from the public, sponsors and indeed the Facebook members, there simply would be no Rescue as this registered charity was solely funded by donations and the good will of the public and that alone. My profound lack of trust with humans had long since been overturned from that very moment I was first brought to Oldham Cats, a helpless little kitten in desperate need of surgery. They didn't turn me away despite my grotesque, neglected state...no not all. The Rescue Managers' words were, "All the more reason to take you in, little fella." And that they did.

Indeed, Oldham Cats was a Rescue that put their felines first and foremost.
My recuperation period at the Hanes household, post-surgery, was indeed the biggest turning point in my life. Short term foster was the initial objective, however, with time and with such progress given, I was clearly going nowhere, nor did I want to. I loved my new family and it wasn't long before Daddy became submissive, agreeing to my adoption. I soon became somewhat of a Mascot for the Rescue via Face Book and the public were requesting regular updates in terms of my progress.

The clutter of dishes brought me back to reality, lots of them. It was feeding time at the Rescue. The cleaning now completed, the sound of volunteers preparing food filled the room, the now impatient meows echoed predominantly. Holly and I snuggled against one another and listened on curiously.

"Toby, come on. That's not yours," Volunteer Sue addressed the black panther, Resident Toby. Not a panther really, but this sleek cat had the grace of one, by all means. My first ever visit to the Rescue, I'll never forget this toothless wonder greeting me curiously from the confinement of my cat carrier. Toby still occasionally sauntered up to our cage, greeting Holly and I, displaying his usual charisma. Toby had been a Resident for years and Mummy told me he was a special boy in many ways. Loved by many, he certainly had his own fan club; even Clare the vet at Crown House had a soft spot for him. You shouldn't have favourites, Mummy told me, but sometimes in life, humans couldn't help such an uncontrollable feeling; human instinct they called it.

So I suppose I had a little human instinct also because this is how I felt about my Baby Holly.

Toby, more than any other Resident cat visited the vets frequently due to his diabetic condition. Mummy told me how brave he was; daily he required insulin injections. Unlike most cats who would walk away, Toby seemed to have a sixth sense that the injections were administered for his benefit. I mean, how many cats would come to you when called for their injection. Certainly not I!

So yes, Toby in my opinion was fearless and brave, a feline to be applauded. Admiration and respect certainly needed to be given also for the way in which he munched through biscuits with gusto, not a single tooth in his mouth.

I couldn't quite grasp why an admirable boy like Toby didn't have a home to call his own until Mummy explained, Resident cats of Oldham Cats were cats who could not be rehomed for various reasons, including health issues. They therefore took residence at the Rescue where they could be cared for and were permitted to freely explore their surroundings. An exceptional life they lived by all accounts; Ginge; Coco; Harry; Jesse; Candy and Maddie.

The sound of suitcase wheels approaching accompanied by a wailing voice distracted my train of thought.

"Aaaaw, good morning my precious boy! Come and see what's on the menu today Toby!"

Volunteer Samantha entered the Adult Room, rustling a bag excitedly.

I nudged Holly.

"Holly, what has she got in the bag today?"

"I'm not quite sure. Hang on..." She approached the front of our cage, straining her head. "Hhhmm, definitely chicken. But prawns I think, also."

Despite the chicken available in our cage, my tummy rumbled some. Samantha's chicken always seemed to taste better for some reason.

The quiet within the room and the sound of volunteer Sue opening cages indicated the felines were now being fed.

The fresh meat and fish Samantha brought to the Rescue were specifically for the residents. However, throughout the morning she would always offer a portion or two to all the cats awaiting their forever homes, Holly and myself included.

"Holly, what on earth does she keep in her wheely thing?" I asked curiously.

"Wool, fundraising items for the Rescue," Holly replied. "Also, lots of wool for Sylvia Barry who knits us our beautiful blankets. She's made hundreds for the Rescue to raise pennies, you know."

"Wow!"

"She's even visited No 10 Downing Street and Larry the cat, with one of her special blankets of course. I heard Mummy telling Daddy." Holly contributed, as always, the font of all knowledge.

"Maybe she'll come in later for another 'kitty fix Holly'. What do you think?" I pondered.

"Oh, she will Jack, she will. As soon as she knows we're here, she'll be in for a cuddle."

The cage door suddenly opened and Sue, now disposed of her tasks, grasped the opportunity to offer us some fuss. I purred loudly.

"You're not such a 'little' Jack anymore are you, eh?" I could hear the smile behind the softly spoken voice and she reached out to stroke me.

"Hey Holly, is she insinuating I have a fat ass too?" I muttered beneath my breath.

"No Jack she's simply saying you've grown some. It's a compliment Jack; stop taking everything so seriously. It means you're becoming a big, strong boy," Holly defended, twitching her whiskers and purring when Sue diverted her strokes to her.

Within time, Sue left, Mummy and the volunteers had moved across to that place called the office, no doubt in need of a well-earned 'cuppa' after cleaning and feeding us furries.

"Where's Mummy been all morning?" I asked, realisation dawning that I'd not seen her for some time. As content as I was at the Rescue, I always relied on her frequent visits to my cage.

"It's kitten rehome day Jack...Don't worry, she's not left us. She's busy, that's all."

A short time later my Mummy approached our cage, scooped me up into her arms and kissed me on my forehead.

"Aaaww Little Jack," she murmured, "Mummy has missed you."

I purred away contentedly, rejoicing in the warmth within Mummy's arms; someone I loved, someone who I trusted. Short-lived this was though as before long Mummy left Holly and I alone yet again, distracted by her work.

The warmth from the window enveloped us both as we snuggled together.

"Holly..."

"Hhhmm, what?" she roused, yawning.

"Tell me what it looks like outside."

She supressed another yawn and gathered her thoughts. "Why, the sun is out now Little Jack."

The sun?

"What does the sun look like Holly? Tell me."

"Well Jack, it's like a great big ball of fire that shines so very brightly. It's beautiful, round and warm and lights everything up."

"Wow! It sounds beautiful." I mused, trying to picture this. "And the rain, I've felt it, but what does that look like?" I prompted.

"Well rain is wet. It's crystal clear Jack and cascades or drizzles or gushes from the sky."

"So, can I walk through it?" I murmured.

"You can...it's almost transparent Jack."

"The wind...what about the wind?"

"You can't see that either Jack, but you can certainly feel it. It's strong and has the capability of blowing things over too."

So, I reflected sadly, the world must be a beautiful place. So much wonder and colour, wonder that I would never see. How amazing it would be to see that great ball of fire in the sky; to see my surroundings; my brood; Mummy or Daddy even.

My world; a blanket of darkness, was so very different and despite living a contented life, wonder and curiosity frequently permeated my thoughts. Sometimes frustration and sadness crept in.

If only...

"Come on now, young chap!" Grandpa Jasper would advise on these occasions, "There's no point feeling like this. What will be will be. Feeling sorry for yourself won't change anything nor will being a victim. You pull yourself together right now. Life is what we make it."

And he was right.

Wise words provided as always from Grandpa Jasper, one of the most respected seniors within our brood. A ginger and white tom of such enormity with a swishing tummy, Grandpa Jasper spent his days lazily in his bed, his body over spilling the confines somewhat.

Grandpa Jasper, like Magic, was a dignified old man, one who had nurtured so many foster babies in the past. One that Holly was quite smitten with, squeezing into his bed and pawing him at every given opportunity.

From the sanctuary of the lounge Grandpa Jasper was indeed an astute old chap, absorbing everything that went on within his surroundings. A cat of such integrity and compassion, he always knew when to offer a helping paw.

"Regard your darkness like a unique gift, Little Jack," Grandpa Jasper once suggested to me, "the use of one's imagination can be far more intriguing and wonderful than the real things in life."

Wise words certainly which made me realise that I was indeed special. Sometimes I would imagine mummy as a princess and my Daddy as a prince. I mentioned this to Holly once and her whiskers twitched as she giggled her response, "Oh little Jack, you couldn't be further from the truth!"

Grandpa Jasper's encouraging words were certainly beneficial, as on many an occasion my imagination drifted away with me. I imagined Simba the Destroyer with horns; Princess Zena with a tiara; Jasper with spectacles; Baby Peanut with a dustbin attached to him and so on.

The familiar sound of the Adult Room door opening and Mummy and Sylvia's voice, suddenly propelled me back to the present. Holly was spooned into me, purring away contentedly.

"Have all the kittens been rehomed now Davina?" Sylvia asked.

"They have, both litters." Mummy replied, approaching my cage.

"Fantastic. Is Holly with Jack?" the excitement in Sylvia's voice was unmistakable.

"She is."

My cage door opened, I knew all too well what was forthcoming; cuddles.

Mummy lifted me gently from the cage and I purred profusely, always welcoming her presence.

"Hello, little man. Mummy's missed you this morning," she murmured, placing a kiss on my head. "Do you want a cuddle with Sylvia?"

I did. Sylvia always cuddled me ever so gently, embracing me in love. I continued to purr as Mummy placed me into the arms of Sylvia...

New beginnings

Nestled into Sylvia's embrace I listened to Holly purr nearby as Mummy cradled her. Mummy had a terrible habit of rocking whilst cuddling our feline kind. Subconsciously she would sway from side to side, embracing these special moments.

So, I thought, it had been kitten rehome day, an explanation for Mummy's absence this morning.

The kitten room; yes, I had spent many a day in there when I was younger. The sound of lactating queens and new born babies suckling would permeate the room, as would the sound of kittens, playing frenetically with one another.

The room had a unique odour, not unpleasant mind; it was a combination of a 'kitten' smell alongside freshly laundered bedding. A smell I was certainly accustomed to.

I'll never forget my first experience, my first night there awaiting the arrival of my foster parents, feeling so alone, confused and contemplating what would become of me.

I had just undergone my surgery; so very tiny and vulnerable yet I somehow knew I was safe, knew everything was going to be all right.

Kitten rehome days, Mummy explained, were often incredibly busy. Sadly, it was always the adult cats that often took longer to rehome, waiting patiently, sometimes pleadingly.

Yes, kittens were most certainly popular and on the date of rehome the Rescue was indeed a hive of activity. On many an occasion Mummy told me people would follow the progress of a kitten or two within a certain litter, anticipating the rehome date. This was often unpredictable, as the volunteers at the Rescue would not rehome any kitten unless it was of the appropriate age, weight, in good health and litter trained. I often wondered how Mummy and the volunteers would judge people appropriate to adopt a kitten...What if they were bad people? What if they intended to harm the kitten?

But Mummy explained this also to me. The adoption process involved a lot of enquiry indeed in relation to suitability and home environments. I should have known better than to even question this, knowing how passionate, dedicated and caring Mummy and all the volunteers were.

On many an occasion people considered unsuitable to adopt a kitten were indeed declined.

The ethos of the Rescue; considering all the fur babies first and foremost, always.

Kitten adoption was simply on a 'first come, first serve' basis and members of the public on several occasions had indeed queued overnight outside the sanctuary of the Rescue, in hope of adopting the kitten of their choice.

Mummy said it was always so rewarding watching kittens and cats go to their forever homes, especially those that had overcome barriers. Barriers she explained could range from health issues to difficult social behaviours in felines. Mummy explained in these situations the team of volunteers would spend relentless time and effort socialising cats and kittens with difficult semi-feral temperaments. Very seldom was there an unsuccessful rehome.

New incredible beginnings were destined for these little ones, a new start in life and for their mummies likewise once neutered.

A happy day indeed for all these babies who can now explore the love and comfort within their new forever homes. Never would I forget that initial feeling of belonging, that feeling of being loved. When Daddy finally agreed to adopt me from foster, well, it was the most incredible feeling ever in the World.

The Rescue has rehomed thousands of felines over the years, changing so many little furbaby lives.

Me, I felt so proud to be one of them.

However, one also needed to consider how many human lives our feline kind have changed, how many people we have touched.

And there were many, my Mummy told me; people who were lonely, people who had suffered a loss, people with mental health issues and people who simply needed the additional companionship within their lives. Indeed, our feline kind have the ability to comfort those who seek our love, committed always to our human slaves.

Baby Peanut was indeed an exemplary example of this. He once told me the tale of how he became one of the Hanes brood. Of course, I was always intrigued and listened on in awe.

"Well, it was two years ago," he told me proudly.

Peanut was a strange, mischievous little ginger character with a bulbous body and a squirrel-like face... a disproportionate little chap indeed.

A glutton he was, always scavenging for food and the first to curl himself around Mummy's ankles come mealtimes. He was indeed the initiator of many of our frolics, a tell-tale within the brood and the one who miraculously always diverted the blame onto one of the others and of course myself. So yes, I was certainly curious to know how Peanut had become a much-loved edition within the Hanes household.

"It was January and Mummy had just suffered the loss of her mum," Peanut said, immersed in thought. "A very dark time it was in Mummy's life, she loved her mum very much and despite her mothers' long-term illness her death came as a sudden shock. Mummy wasn't in a good place at all despite the support from her family and the brood of course. She wouldn't go out of the house other than to deal with funeral arrangements and wouldn't, couldn't talk to anyone beyond her close family. Every day was a miserable existence for her for some time as grief, loss, pain and sadness dominated everything else in her life. Days rolled into weeks and her depressive state worsened, the tears never abating. It was at this point she heard of my pregnant mummy having been rescued and taken into foster by Julie who worked at Crown House Vets. My feline mummy had escaped a fire from a fire training exercise at a Fire Station. She had been nesting in a box and miraculously escaped the small fire unhurt, fortunately the firemen noticed her and once rescued, they gave her oxygen. Despite slight smoke inhalation and a coat that was chargrilled and grey, she was in good health and we all survived, still cocooned in Mummy's womb. Upon hearing of this, Mummy contacted Julie and offered to foster my mother and she named her Ellie, in memory of her mum."

"Surely Mummy had enough things going on without fostering?" I asked.
"Well you know Mummy." Peanut sighed, "She loves fostering mums and babies and maybe she thought this would help her some in her current state; you know, something to focus on. On the 8th March we were born. Ellie was such a trusting cat and allowed Mummy Davina to stay with her throughout the birth. My Mummy Ellie had a normal birth, she delivered five kittens including myself and everything seemed to be going fine with me and my ginger siblings…that was until day three…"
Peanut paused, immersed in thought.
"Why, what went wrong on day three?" I queried, not sure if I was going to like Peanut's answer at all.
"Mummy walked into our room that morning to find only four babies instead of five. Frantically, she searched under the bedding within the confines of Mummy Ellie's cage. Nothing. Out of the corner of her eye, she noticed a still tiny body camouflaged against the wooden flooring…"
"Oh no Peanut! You mean one of them died…"
"It was me…"
"But…"

"Let me finish!" Peanut huffed impatiently. "You see, me being ever the explorer and the tiniest of kittens, far tinier than my siblings, well, I was frantic to get to Mummy Ellie's teats and at some point, during the night I slipped through the cage bars. I was cold and lifeless when Mummy did finally discover me in the morning.

Mummy desperately tried to revive me, breathing into my mouth and massaging my lifeless body to generate some warmth. My tiny, shallow breaths disintegrated into nothing. Mummy had helped revive other tiny babies in the past, sometimes successfully, on other occasions with no luck, but in her current state of depression this really did upset her. Defeated, shoulders slumped she finally wrapped my lifeless body in a fleece, close to her chest.

'I tried little one,' she said to me *'Run free now'*. Minutes passed.

Silence.

I could almost feel the weight of Mummy's impending doom and depression, her sadness and hurt. Then, with a sharp gasp, I began to wriggle. Mummy, startled, began to desperately warm me some more..."

"Wow Peanut, you survived!" I gasped in awe, "How brave!"

"Of course. Brave that's what I am...brave!" Peanuts whiskers twitched and his head was raised with pride as he told his story. He paused momentarily to dip into the biscuit bowl and crunch on a few biscuits.

Appetite appeased, he continued, "Have you ever wondered where the name Peanut derived from? I was named Peanut because I was so tiny I resembled a nut kernel!"

"That's kind of cute." I smiled to myself.

"Things weren't easy though at the beginning...I was miniscule in comparison to the rest of my siblings and needed supplementing quite heavily from Mummy Davina. I just struggled so much getting to Mummy Ellie's teats, my siblings were much bigger and stronger than myself. I had setbacks also as a young kitten, my intestines were enlarged and I went through a period where I was quite poorly. My tummy was so large, my whole body resembled a football."

It still does I thought, but felt the need for a little tact.

"I looked like the greedy inflated Veruca Salt character from that Willy Wonker story. Mummy thought she was going to lose me at one point, but as brave as I am, I soldiered on..."

"Is this why you have an inflated tummy and you walk with a strange swagger?" I asked curiously.

"Now, now! Enough said about the belly thank you," Peanut retorted indignantly. "Anyway, as you can imagine mummy and I developed a special bond throughout all of that and adopting me was such an inevitable outcome."

"You said you helped mummy through a difficult period Peanut, I don't understand. It seems like all the focus was on helping you." I twitched my whiskers, confused.

"Don't you understand Little Jack, when I say us felines help humans, I really mean that. I gave Mummy a purpose, I gave her a reason to get out of bed every morning, I provided her with motivation and her dependency on me was as important as my dependency on her. As much as no one could ever take away her sorrow and her loss, I became a very healthy distraction indeed. Mummy Hanes is just a tiny example of how much us felines can make a real difference to human lives."

"Now I understand." I murmured.

And that was the moment I realised just how much animals, any animal, can change the lives of human individuals for the better, how we can provide our human masters such companionship, how we can provide them a purpose in life and how we can help them overcome barriers...

The day at the Rescue passed like a whirlwind, they always did, and not before too long Holly and I were back within the sanctuary of our home. No sooner had Mummy opened our carrier, when Holly and I jumped out and were greeted by bountiful purrs, meows, sniffs and rubs.

Holly's first mission was to go and greet Grandpa Jasper who was of course residing in his larger than average bed.

"Come on then little cherub, come and tell me all about the Rescue today?" he encouraged with a purr. So that was Holly distracted for some time.

Tea times always propelled us all into a hive of activity; the rattle of dishes bringing the household to life. Appetites satisfied, we all took position in our favourite comfort zones within the home.

Magic, Thor and Tiddles all lay next to Mummy who sprawled on the sofa. Pepper, Zena , Peanut and Max lazily lounged along the back rest.

I clambered somewhat recklessly onto Mummy's knee as she typed away on her laptop.

"What's she playing at?" Simba the Destroyer frowned, his wide sceptical eyes glaring over Mummy's shoulder.

"Mummy's writing a story about me and all of you. Mummy seems to think she can get this published."

"Ridiculous!" Simba retorted superciliously. "A real book! Never!"

Well, Simba was surely a story by himself, I thought. There was certainly a tale or two be told about Simba's mischievous antics.

I enveloped myself into my Mummy's arms as she typed away, nudging the keyboard every now and then, when her strokes lessened. A little book about me I still couldn't quite believe it! but Mummy was driven, completely focused.

True to her word, every night she clicked away on that keyboard, immersed in her thoughts; some memories were enveloped in happiness, others were shrouded in sadness.

Building Bridges

Relationships within our feline brood were amazing and we had long since developed a mutual respect for one another. Following my initial arrival, within time, the other felines grew accepting of my peculiar little characteristics and antics.

I would frequently walk with my head lowered, my whiskers guiding me and when unfamiliar objects presented themselves in the home I would curiously and with trepidation lift up my front paw to examine these alien things.

The others of course, would explore anything and everything with immediate gusto, they would overtake me; tails swishing, their lithe and swift bodies confident during their explorations. When I say lithe bodies, well this was with the exception of some of the brood who were proportionately obese; they would clumsily topple over the smaller scratch posts and with time weaken the heavy-duty cat trees with their robust frames…Countess Tiddula Tiddles, Magic, Thor, Peanut and Pepper were all indeed guilty culprits.

Grandpa Jasper, during the years he had lived at the Hanes, had never explored a cat tree and seldom attempted the stairs. A content old man he was who loved his home comforts.

"C'mon Jasper, climb with me," I once pleaded.

"No child, you carry on," he replied with a yawn, "Go and have some fun with the others. I'm too old and tired for such frolics." Of course, he would never disclose that the enormity of his frame was most possibly a mitigating factor towards such laziness. Indeed, Grandpa Jasper, the delightful old soul, was more than content to lounge and watch us play.

Intrigued, I once asked Grandpa Jasper how he became adopted into the Hanes family.

"Well child, sadly my last owners left me behind when they moved. Devastated I was, simply devastated. I really thought I was part of the family; that they wanted me forever and would love me unconditionally. But no, they simply deserted me. My whole world came crashing down," Jasper paused, clearly reminiscing some. "I was living from scraps of food for some time, that's before I was rescued and taken to Oldham Cats where they made me available for adoption. An older boy, I didn't attract much attention from the public despite my affectionate nature and rumbling purrs. It was April time and fortunately for me, Mummy and Daddy had decided to get another cat as a companion for Magic. I could hear them chatting as they looked at all the other cats awaiting adoption. I anticipated the moment they approached my cage wondering would they pass me by like many of the others did. Surreal somehow, they drew to a halt once they reached me."

"HE'S a big handsome lad," Daddy exclaimed, peering into my cage.

"Um, I don't know," Mummy hesitated, "I've never really thought about having a ginger and white cat."

"It's a colour Davina, that's all! Don't be bloody ridiculous...What the hell has colour got to do with anything? Just listen to him purr!" Daddy snapped.

Mummy took a step closer guiltily and read my history on the card attached to my cage.

"Aaaw, how could they just leave you behind?" Mummy murmured.

Then she made that fatal mistake.

She turned to volunteer Sue and asked if she could take me out of the cage for a further look. The rest became history, Jack. No looking back on my past life, not ever."

"So, we've all had a difficult past life then haven't we Jasper? Not just me." More of a rhetorical question escaped my lips.

"Indeed, we have, young man. Not to dwell though, little one, as we now live our days in splendour," Jasper replied, more upbeat.

"Jasper tell me about your role as mentor to the foster babies?" I asked curiously. "I mean, all the new kids on the block always seem to gravitate towards you. Why, I wonder?"

"Well, young man, I daresay they sense a wise old man when they see one. I think the layers of my extended tummy indeed provide additional warmth also," Jasper drawled proudly. "A gentle, loving personality and a kind soul it takes when allowing these little tinkers to suckle and curl their tiny bodies beside you. The first foster baby I ever helped was a tiny black kitten called Dusty. Mummy called him that because he was found on the rubbish tip Christmas Eve."

"Dusty?"

"Wake up, Jack!... dear me! Dusty, you know, as in dusty bin because he was found on the rubbish tip. She brought him home until the New Year so that he wouldn't be confined to a cage on his own at the Rescue."

"Kittens always get homes though. Why didn't anyone want to adopt him?" I wrinkled my brow, puzzled.

"Oldham Cats won't rehome kittens over the Christmas period." Jasper explained, "So little Dusty came home, little cracker he was. Must say I was a tad smitten with this one, and the feeling was certainly reciprocated. Even Daddy had a real soft spot for him, but Mummy put her foot down, saying (at that point) four cats were far too many. Tiddles was already on the scene. Dusty did eventually go to a good home though, so I believe. Daddy never forgave Mummy for this decision; still doesn't to this day. He loved little Dusty. I suppose Mummy was doing what she thought was right at the time."

I gulped. Four cats! My, my! Mummy certainly had since changed her outlook in terms of acceptability of cats with a now superlative brood of 13, including myself.

Similarly to humans, we had our own special bonds with one another; our very own 'cliques' so to speak. With differing characteristics and temperaments, we were incredibly diverse and such diversity sometimes provoked tempestuous relationships.

Holly and I were an entity together and throughout the year she had indeed become my mentor, my guide and indeed my eyes. Through learned behaviour I had long since mastered the cat trees and I knew my boundaries...sometimes, that is, sometimes.

I would climb, claw, swoop and jump confidently as I manoeuvred my way around the cat trees, each level mapped out in my mind. During robust play, I would often dangle precariously, becoming over-excited by our mischievous frolics. The only one I needed to be sceptical about bumping into was Simba the Destroyer and he didn't take lightly to my clumsiness, in fact he didn't take lightly to anyone of us at all.

Simba the Destroyer was indeed a volatile character, one whom you needed to appease, or better still, keep your distance from whilst he was on the prowl. I'd obviously had several tempestuous encounters myself with him, not knowing until it was too late that I was stumbling into the 'lion's den'.

Inquisitively, I questioned Grandpa Jasper over Simba.

"So, Grandpa, what's the story with Simba, the bad ass?"

"Mind your language Little Jack!" Jasper reprimanded curtly with a gentle swipe of his paw.

"But Thor says it..."

"...Never you mind young man who says what! Your Mummy and Daddy would be mortified knowing you used such foul language. Keep your innocence Little Jack, dear me, nothing gained in being influenced."

I purred my defeat.

"Well, that Simba, I despair some." Grandpa Jasper twitched his whiskers and I could feel his rolls of fat shudder. "Brought him up myself I did when he arrived as a mere kitten some years ago. A lovely little chap he was, worshipped by Mummy and Daddy's human daughter Cerys and of course the rest of the family. I embraced him with love and a firm paw just like I do all the others and just look what a rogue he's become now. He does nothing other than treat me with confrontation at every given opportunity. I really don't know what's become of him..." Jasper drifted off, deep in thought.

"Are his eyes really so big Grandpa?" I asked, intrigued.

"Big, round prowling eyes they are. A handsome tabby I must say but those eyes, well, they're constantly alert, seeking and searching for mischief." Jasper sighed despairingly.

Peanut swaggered past us towards the conservatory, not before stopping and spooning his face into mine with a cheeky meow; his invitation to play of course. Daddy was currently engrossed in the square box called the television and Mummy was clicking away on her laptop; each had their own sofa, draped with the lazier cats within the brood. Permanent dips in the backrest of the sofas were testimony to how much time they actually spent there...and I'm making reference to the other cats, not Mummy and Daddy!

The conservatory had indeed, more so during my stay, become a haven for the brood and myself; long gone were some of the more prestigious and elegant ornaments that once adorned the room. The room now had predominantly become a playroom for all us furries to languish in with copious amounts of toys and scratch trees, of which I had long since mastered the art of climbing.

Mummy's days of displaying her fine ornaments in this very room were replaced by her boasting her fur babies at play.

Mummy had always worked hard to enjoy her small luxuries in life and I often wondered whether my Daddy or herself ever had regrets in terms of their change in lifestyles and indeed their priorities with such a brood of rescue cats, albeit superlative.

I shouldn't have even ever questioned their love or devotion to us though, not ever. Mummy, ever our protector, was besotted with us. Her home, her little sanctuary had become our world all together. Magic said her face beamed whenever she spoke of us and indeed such love was reciprocated. We had a family, all of us, a family who loved us for our qualities and indeed imperfections.

Daddy's love for me was also unprecedented, as much, as I recall his initial hesitance in terms of adopting me during the beginning. My surreptitious quest of making him love me soon took shape and within no time he submitted and told Mummy I could stay with them forever.

Daddy's love for me turned into something far, far bigger than I'd ever contemplated and there were many an occasion where I'd witness both Mummy and Daddy baiting one another over me.

There would be the occasions where I would sprawl lazily on Mummy's knee and jealous Daddy would purposefully call my name to disturb our special moments.

Then there were many episodes during which I would be playing with my Daddy and perplexed, Mummy would bulldoze her way into the room with a far more elaborate toy to divert my attention.

"Spiteful, that's what you are Davi...bloody spiteful! You could see we were having fun!" Daddy would snap.

"Sorry I didn't realise," Mummy often replied airily.

Clearly their love for me went without question and with such banter and competition between the two, I never went short of attention.

Back to the present and with a confident swagger I followed the rambunctious Peanut into the conservatory. He was already immersed in play with Little Man Max on one of the scratch trees. The meowing, swinging, thudding and banging from up above seemed incredibly enticing.

"C'mon buddy! Join in," Little Man Max invited.

Without further hesitation, I latched onto the cat tree post and began to climb excitedly.

Crash!

I ambled straight into Little Man Max.

"HEY! SLOW DOWN!" he reprimanded me impatiently with a swift bat of his paw.

Chuckling, Peanut watched on, now on the top tier. "Jack, come and get me!" he teased.

I raised my head and meowed chirpily, knowing the exact spot where he would be.

"Stop teasing him Peanut," Little Man Max grunted in frustration, jumping to another layer on the tree.

My one eyed wide, my ears and whiskers pricked forward as I angled my body in preparation to pursue Little Man Max. I lowered my body and the end of my tail and hindquarters twitched in anticipation.

1,2,3...

With precision I landed on the right cat perch and within seconds Little Man Max's body and mine were coiled as we playfully nipped one another during our somewhat predatory game of play aggression.

"Getting a little too ahead of yourself now little Jack!" Little Man Max chuckled and with a body slam he had me pinned beneath him.

"Not at all…" I gasped breathlessly.

Peanut chided from the perch up ahead, "Go on, Little Jack, take a swing to the right, that way you can take him out! Max that's pathetic, take a punch to the left!"

Ever the instigator, he refereed from above whilst we bashed, crashed, swooped and coiled before finally tumbling to the ground just as if we were in a wrestling ring.

"Round two!" Peanut exclaimed with excitement. Although I couldn't see my audience, with the ability and concept of extrasensory perception, I knew they were present…the others were indeed watching. Not all of them, but most of them, our audience waited in anticipation.

"A bloody pitiful show!" Simba the Destroyer scoffed. "Absolutely pathetic."

"Don't be such a miserable bad ass!" Thor retorted sharply.

"Thor, you mind that language, young man!" Grandpa Jasper interceded from his humungous bed, which was situated in the lounge.

"Honestly, he needs to give the kid a break," Thor defended. "What with no eyes…"

"…I have one!" I gasped breathlessly as Little Max Max suddenly stung me with an unexpected blow to my right.

"Yes, but it serves no purpose really, does it?" Simba muttered, his body coiled lazily on the sofa.

With Max momentarily distracted, I used my ginger hunk strength and swiftly performed a series of cunning predatory manoeuvres to thwart my opponent.

Stunned, defeated even, Max took a step back yet I could sense the admiration from him.

"Bravo!" Peanut announced from his perch above. "Today we have our new champion, Little Jack. Round of a-paws everyone!"

I could indeed sense the admiration from the crowd as they circled, watching on.

"Oh, that's my boy!" Holly purred dreamily.

And so, it was constant feline predatory frolics like this that really had begun to earn me much respect. Simba was indeed a confrontational character and often a loner...the brood and myself had long since accepted his territorial and volatile characteristics. There were times where he would surprise us with the odd show of feline affection but these occasions were few and far between.

Simba had a love for the human slaves in the household, but even then, he would only reciprocate their love and affection when it suited him.

Many a morning I would hear Daddy exclaim, "He's done it again Davina! Weed all over my work clothes!"

"More fool you for leaving them on the floor," Mummy would always defend. "You know what Simba's like."

Mummy however, was not quite as understanding on the occasions she went to work only too late to realise Simba had urinated in her handbag and in her boots!

So as a preventive measure in the Hanes household, clothes always needed folding away, towels needed appropriate storage and bags, of any shape or size, needed closing or hiding. Did they love Simba any less for his bizarre antics and mischievous frolics? was sometimes my prevailing question? Simba was on par with a child in a class who always failed to make the appropriate choices in life; always had something to prove and would go to any length to prove that point.

I once, however, eavesdropped into a family debate, which put my curiosity to rest.

The daughters Chanel and Cerys were home to visit from University; I always welcomed the additional attention and fuss they offered me during their visits. Their shock of my initial arrival at home some months ago soon dispersed within no time and had been replaced by only what one could describe as love, admiration and respect for me. On this particular occasion, Simba, with his extra predatory streak of defiance, seized the opportunity to attack dear old Grandpa Jasper as he pottered by innocently in the lounge.

With a startled yelp, Jasper backed himself into a corner of the room.

Simba, when things didn't quite go his way, (like not being the first to poo in one of the litter trays or not getting his place on the sofa) would often retaliate and unfortunately on this occasion poor old Jasper was within Simba's radar.

"Simba!" Daddy bolted from the kitchen; Mummy ran downstairs and Chanel sprinted from the sofa to tend to Jasper. I was on Cerys's knee, ears pricked and tail bristled still from the shrill distressed cry from the old man.

Jasper, unharmed, was now being comforted by Chanel, and Simba the nomad, guiltily left the scene of disruption.

"You ok, Grandpa?" I whispered.

"I am son, thank you. Just startled me some and at my age I have to take care of the old ticker! Good lord, I didn't see that one coming!" Jasper replied.

"I'll go after him for Grandpa," I offered heroically but praying Grandpa Jasper wouldn't take up my premature offer of being the hero.

"No, son. You stay here," Grandpa Jasper mumbled whilst purring away to his humans.

"When is he going to stop this?" Daddy addressed mummy harshly. "I'm fed up with Simba doing...."

"Stop there!" Mummy retorted sharply and my ears pricked even further with her tone, "...Yes Simba does have issues, yes he does cause chaos but within the mainstream of things, there's an equilibrium..."

"You can't give up on him!" Cerys interjected," he's MY cat!"

"Then take him with you..." Daddy snapped.

"Oh boy! They're really cross, Grandpa," I frowned.

"My dear boy, this conversation has been relayed time and time again," Jasper consoled as he squashed his large frame into his supersize bed. "No harm done, little one, no harm whatsoever..."

And the humble beast resided peacefully within the confines of his custom fit bed.

"What next?" Daddy persisted. "He's already demolished the furniture! And now he's having a go at the others! Then there's..."

"Stop!" Mummy's deadly tone silenced the room.

Even the daughters watched on in silence.

"Would you ever give up your child?" Mummy confronted Daddy, her tone dangerously low. "Did you ever consider giving up Chanel and Cerys when they were naughty as children?"

The silence was broken by Cerys's disgruntled tone, "Seriously, us, naughty...?"

"...Well, um, no." Daddy offered reluctantly.

"Then Simba's no different is he? Try to focus on his good qualities...and there are many."

"Chanel and Cerys never ate through furniture, weed on things or chased one another around the home though, did they?" More of a rhetorical question from Daddy.

Chanel, now immersed in the square television, obviously had her ears tuned in to the debate, "Well, now that you mention it Dad, little do you know..." Her voice trailed off purposefully.

"He's part of the family Dad and he's my cat! He can't help it. I swear, you ever rehome Simba and I'll never forgive you...I'll never come home again!"

"I didn't say that Cerys. It's just that..." Daddy's voice trailed off helplessly, the women evidently outnumbered him. He patted Jasper on the head and defeated somewhat, returned to the kitchen to resume his duties.

"Hey Grandpa!" I whispered. "What does this mean? Is Simba staying then, or are they rehoming him?"

"He's here for the long haul Little Jack, indeed he is," Grandpa Jasper sighed. "Mother Hanes is strong in her belief that sometimes one must ride the storm." He paused momentarily and emphasised the parenthesis in his next words, knowing his beliefs are respected, "Simba does, I believe, indeed have some endearing qualities and it's those qualities we must remember, all of us. Don't be fooled by his robust exterior, Little Jack, he has his gentle moments. Simba's in need of a home full of love and affection just like the rest of us. Let us not deny him this."

Feeling guilty somewhat for my aversion to Simba, I reflected on Jaspers words. I jumped from Cery's knee, the hideous music she was playing irritating me some. I could hear Mummy tapping away on the laptop from the other sofa. A manoeuvre I made to the left, then a swift to the right as I carefully approached her. Each step I took with precision, knowing the room plan with such confidence now. Paw outstretched, I gently tapped until I made contact with Mummy's leg then with force I hoisted myself up onto her lap. The laptop was soon disregarded as Mummy averted her attention to me.

"Come on then little fella, cuddle time," Mummy said softly as I positioned myself correctly on her knee. As she stroked and petted me, I chirped contently, kneading her legs.

Yes, guiltily I admonished myself for my thoughts regarding Simba. Grandpa Jasper was quite right. Who was I to judge and to sometimes even question his role and indeed presence within the family? His frenetic moods and volatile play were characteristics we had all become accustomed to, and yes, he did have an affectionate nature, thus, when it benefited him, of course.

I had long since developed bonds within the brood and with sadness I sometimes wished Simba would participate in our frenzied frolics but sadly this wasn't the case to be...his nomadic tendencies clearly defined him as one who simply enjoyed his own company and that of his human slaves.

This we needed to respect; and indeed, rejoice in his shows of affection to us when they came, which they did, on his terms of course.

Simba just needed love and care, just as we all did.

Little did I know at this point in my life the changes I would face ahead...

Independence day

Pelting, tumbling, spooning and nipping, guiding, cuddling, washing and purring...Yes, Holly and I shared many a treasured moment together and still continue to do so. Baby Holly guided me in life, she always did, always stayed by my side and when not, she remained within the peripheral radar. As a vulnerable, confused, blind kitten, she had become my vision in life, my mentor and my very, very dear friend. She taught me much of everything I knew; how to manoeuvre around the home with confidence, how to trust, how to play safely and certainly how to master the art of climbing the cat trees.
Often, I would dangle precariously after missing my footing and always she would be there by my side...chirping and purring, her cry to help me. And that she did.
Our visits to the Rescue were always harmonious, together we would squash into the carrier with our growing frames and together we would graciously accept and welcome the attention and cuddles offered to us. Always, I remained by Holly's side.

It was a Sunday morning and Mummy was typing away on her laptop. Daddy was occupied working in the house, busying himself as per usual.
Holly and I cuddled beside one another on the comfort of the sofa.
"Jack..."
"...Hhmm?" I roused sleepily.
"Do you think it's time to spread your wings now, little man?"
I could hear the hesitance in her tone, almost as if she was afraid to offend me.
"Spread my wings? I don't know what you mean..." my voice trailed off as I lay there confused.

"I mean, explore some more without me being your constant shadow, Jack. Don't get me wrong, I love being with you and want to be with you... I'll still be with you, forever, but you have the confidence and ability to explore some, more independently, now Jack." Holly explained.

My whiskers tilted miserably, mouth pouted, I barely managed my words, "You mean you don't want to be my friend anymore...?"

"Oh no Jack, nothing of the sort!" Holly gasped and spooned herself closer to me. "I'll always, always be your special friend. It's just that you've made so many friends in the brood now. You really need to enjoy each other to your full potential...you know... explore more! You don't want me as your constant shadow when you can also have so much fun with the others. Not that I mind you being with me, not at all, I love you being with me. I just don't want to hold you back." Holly explained.

Wounded by her words, I scrambled from the sofa, my head lowered pitifully as I made my way through to the hallway and up the stairs.

"JACK! COME BACK!..." Holly pleaded guiltily.

I ignored her of course and heard Jasper reprimand Holly from behind me. With careful calculation, I mounted the stairs.

"Absolutely no tact Holly! None whatsoever. Just think before you speak. That poor chap is so upset now..."

"Typical woman thing if you ask me," Simba muttered.

"Well no one did ask you! Keep your butt out!" Holly snapped irritably.

"Hey Jack..."

"What's up Jack?"

"What's happened Jack?"

Curious purrs emanated from some of the brood as I shuffled past them and made my way into the bedroom.

Feeling dejected, I clambered onto the bed nearby Candy and Magic who slept peacefully.

How could Holly be so cruel? Such cruel, horrid words! She'd had enough of me obviously… had enough of me shadowing her all the time I thought glumly. My body slumped and I let out a deflated sigh.

Morning evolved into afternoon and still I lay there, drifting in and out of sleep and sulking over my abandoned state.

Footsteps approached and instantaneously I knew they belonged to Daddy.

"Hey buddy, you're not your usual self today. What's to do?" he asked as he sat beside me.

Frustrated, I wanted to tell him, wanted him to understand what Holly had said to me.

Despite the communication barrier between cats and humans, Daddy had certainly identified I lacked my usual charisma today. Mummy and Daddy knew me well and could often establish when I was poorly or when was indeed affected by someone or something… someone like Holly, I thought glumly as Daddy stroked me.

The sound of Candy and Magic rang in my ears; their close friendship tormenting my dull mood even further.

"Take it somewhere else," I muttered.

Candy stilled momentarily then the mattress dipped as she angled her body closer to mine.

"Right come on then Little Jack, spill the beans… A problem shared is a problem halved," she insisted, her whiskers tickling my face.

Magic steered forward, his ears pricking in suspense.

"You won't understand," I whispered.

"Sulking like this won't do any good," Magic advised, "and it creates a bad atmosphere. If one's upset, then it becomes a snowball effect, others become upset. We don't want Simba upsetting now, do we?"

No, we didn't.

It was with reluctance I told them about Holly and all the hurtful things she'd said to me.

"Oh Jack! Don't you understand? Holly hasn't fallen out with you at all. Is this what this sulking is all about?"

"But…"

"She's simply saying that a little exploration of your own will be good for you and will help you build relationships with us all. Of course, she still wants to be your friend, my dear!" Candy exclaimed.

"She does?" I widened my one eye in surprise.

"Oh Jack, wake up!" Magic intervened, "Who was always there for you from the very beginning? Holly loves you and wants the very best for you. You must understand this. From young, she's carried you, helped you, loved you and now she wants you to become more independent Jack…. She'll always be your girl. It's not a big deal."

Candy edged towards Magic with her usual predatory claim over him, "Just look at us two. There's many a time we give each other a little space despite the fact we have this, um, thing for each other."

Magic grimaced his embarrassment.

A wave of guilt washed over me…impulsive that's what I'd been today, impulsive and over reactive. My first ever experience at feeling wounded by Holly's words made me appreciate the magnitude of how words can profoundly hurt…more prevailing from today was how words and actions can indeed be misinterpreted.

You see, similarly to humans, us felines had feelings and moods also. We had our 'off days' where our moods would spiral beyond control and could subsequently affect our behaviours.

Me? I realised I'd over reacted some over the incident with Holly. How ridiculous of me! I should have known better; appreciated that she wanted only the best for me.

Humbled, with my tail lowered, I submissively began my decent down the stairs to find Holly.

I had to say sorry.

Holly of course welcomed me with open paws... always my special friend and accomplice in life.

We spent the remainder of the evening curled into one another contently, apologetically even.

Another turning point in my tiny life. I'd learned what it felt like to be hurt; how humbling it was to forgive; how it felt to be honest about your own shortfalls and indeed acceptance that I had friendships beyond Holly.

Daddy took his usual position on the sofa, mesmerised by the noisy square box that his eyes were so frequently glued to.

Mummy gathered her papers that were strewn over the table haphazardly.

"I'm going up now," she announced, supressing a yawn.

"It's early still." Daddy objected, "Why not give it a break for the night?"

"No, I want the transcript submitted to Lionel by next week. Almost there now."

The book, my little book and Lionel, the publisher, was the reason Mummy spent so many discreet evenings within the sanctuary of her study, typing away and responding to emails.

I knew only too well, as I would wait for her until the early hours of the morning sometimes, taking my usual position at the foot of the bed, waiting for her to retire. Working full time, she devoted her evenings to writing so this was a temporary change, I needed to become accustomed to.

"It won't be for long," Mummy would say many an evening and she would kiss me on my forehead. "Let's pray your little book is liked and can make some pennies for the babies at the Rescue."

True to her word Mummy reached her objective and 'The Life of Little Jack', my very own little book, was in its final stages of being processed the following week.

"How do I promote it?" Mummy asked Faye worriedly during one of her visits to the house, "What if people don't like it? What if…"

"Stop the worrying woman!" Faye diverted her attention from me, cutting Mummy short. I circled and sniffed her cat-scented ankles whilst she continued talking.

"People have followed Little Jack so much and many have really expressed an interest in his book. Have a little faith in yourself Davina…We do."

I twitched my whiskers and chirped proudly…a little book about me. Still dubious of those cat-scented ankles, I continued to circle Faye's feet.

"What about a book launch day at the Rescue?" Mummy suggested.

"I think we should make a day of it. A celebration of Little Jack," Faye replied and I listened on attentively as the two discussed the logistics of the event in question.

"I'll take Little Jack of course but I don't want him alone…" Mummy pondered, "certainly Holly too. And maybe Peanut I think, as they've developed quite a bond."

Peanut swaggered closer within earshot.

"Hey, it's about time I got some public attention back after you stole my thunder Jack!" he twittered into my ear.

"I didn't…"

"Did! I'm not quite normal too you know, deserving of some publicity I think. I can just see it right now…the paparazzi all over me whilst I pose and purr, flash lights hitting me from every angle."

Peanut immersed himself into a train of thought, in a cloud of surrealism.

"Yes, I think Peanut will enjoy the experience," Mummy confirmed. "He'll love the fuss I'm sure."

Hhhhmmm....

The date of the book launch finally arrived; Mummy was pleased with the publication, somewhat proud, even.

The morning of the launch escalated into a hive of activity at home. Mummy liaised with Faye on that object called a mobile...Faye tended to the finer details; the celebration cakes, the refreshments, the banners and indeed the preparation for our chalet. Other volunteers likewise offered their time and support for my little event.

Clanging; the cat carriers appeared and many of the brood scurried away, all too familiar with the sound.

Holly and myself were accustomed to the carriers and indeed our journeys to the Rescue and submissively we allowed ourselves to be placed in the carriers.

Peanut was a different story!

Scratching, clawing and hissing he proved to be the proverbial coward as he was placed unceremoniously into his carrier.

"Peanut, that's utterly pathetic." I whispered, "You're embarrassing yourself. I thought you was the brave one..."

"...I get it." Holly intervened from within her own confined space, "You're all talk! Mummy's boy deep down, aren't you!"

"Am not..." he hissed and spat defensively.

Mummy was far too preoccupied in drowning herself in the putrid perfume and applying paint to her face, she failed to notice Peanuts resistance.

"Hey good luck young man," Grandpa Jasper said sincerely as he pottered over to my carrier. "Well deserved little man...and remember Little Jack, everyone who shows up today is to offer their support for you and the Rescue. The proceeds from your book will help many more."

"I suppose it's good luck from me too," Simba muttered reluctantly as he sauntered past, "Show them what you're made of."

An encore of well wishes emanated from the brood as we were transported out of the house.

The journey for Holly and myself proved to be very much like what we were accustomed to other than the disruption that took place in the front of the car. Mummy had Peanut's carrier on her knee.

"Crickey Peanut!" Mummy complained. "There's no need for this fuss, little fella."

Growling, hissing and spitting Peanut drowned the sound of the radio throughout the journey.

"You're being silly." Holly exclaimed.

"He's not," I defended, "He's worried. Remember, many of his visits previously had been to the vets when he was poorly." I paused and turned to Peanut, "It's ok really Peanut, just a nice day ...everything will be ok."

Peanut growled his acute frustration in return.

The book launch itself evolved into something unprecedented. A flock of people arrived to support my book, each and every one supporting the Rescue and indeed my little journey so far. Mummy, immersed in book signing and speaking to our wonderful supporters, constantly had her eye on us in the large chalet.

I clumsily yet curiously pottered around my alien surroundings, somewhat intrigued and lavishing in all the attention; Holly performed a series of feline acrobatic moves and welcomed all the fuss given whereas Peanut hissed and spat irritably within the confines of the chalet.

Mummy set everything aside and sat with us for some time.

"Come on now little buddy," she encouraged, "I thought you'd enjoy this. People are looking forward to meeting you too."

"She's right," I tried to console him further. "Remember your vision of being in the spotlight, well here's your chance Peanut to shine."

"Yeah, you don't want attention for the WRONG reasons now do you?" Holly interjected, dangling precariously from one of the cat trees.

Silence ensured whilst she twisted, turned and somersaulted with an agility that put both Peanut and myself to shame.

"Anyway...what happened to Peanut the almighty brave one; the instigator?" she taunted.

"It's okay Peanut, really, everything's okay... Don't be afraid. They're good people here. She's just teasing you." Shaking my head, I consoled Peanut then diverted my attention back to Holly.

"You're not helping matters here at all. You need to remember Holly, some of us have had it harder than you. Peanut had a really difficult beginning..."

"...So did I," Holly defended, "I was syringe fed also you know!"

"It's not just about the hand rearing Holly..."

"...It's okay really," Peanut insisted, "I'm alright. Just a bit overwhelmed, that's all. I guess I'm a home bird at the end of the day. Listen you two; not a word to the others back home. You understand? I have a reputation to keep."

He shuffled his paws and twitched his whiskers agitatedly, circling Mummy, who despite her futile human attempts, was somewhat of a hindrance, pussy footing around as she frequently did.

"This goes nowhere, you promise? They'd make a bloody meal of this back home!" Peanut held his bulbous, stocky frame rigidly whilst he addressed us both. "Hey! It's your special day though Jack, let's make this happen,"

"I promise to keep quiet." I reassured. "Umm...and thank you, really."

"I won't breathe a word, I guess." Holly proceeded to somersault through the air with her usual agility and confidence, "It's between us three."

The day proceeded well; Peanut, despite his inner fears, frequently approached the front of the chalet as onlookers and supporters so dearly wanted to meet him in person. Holly was alike, subject to lots of fuss and the confident girl she was, she rejoiced from the onslaught of attention.

Myself, I suppose being blind, I should have felt bewildered some, but no, this was a place in which I felt comfortable, loved even. The people here wanted to support our good cause. I could tell by the way in which they approached; the manner in which they spoke.

"Holly, is there a good turnout of people?" I twitched my whiskers, hearing a lot of activity beyond our chalet but obviously the blanket of darkness made it difficult for me to determine just how busy and successful the book launch was. The welcomed endearments from supporters as they peeked into our chalet made me feel quite special indeed and I welcomed these throughout the course of the day.

"Jack, it's really busy. There are lots and lots of people here."

"Are they buying my book Holly?" I asked inquisitively.

"They are Jack; they are!"

I smiled to myself, "Mummy will be pleased."

"Aaaaw Jack, you want to see Daddy, he looks pathetic...dressed up as a giant cat he is!" Peanut giggled, his tempestuous mood had abated some.

"Mummy's sister Shell is here too and even her Daddy Brian. All the volunteers are here to support her and even some of Mummy's friends have come along. Lots and lots of supporters and friends are here Jack, it's awesome!"

Frustrated, I wish I could have seen this with my very own eyes, but I was relieved and grateful for such an incredible show of support nonetheless. Mummy had worked so hard to achieve this in aid of raising pennies for the furries at the Rescue...in fact, we all had!

We had certainly paid a penance too with lost cuddle times due to all the hours Mummy spent immersing herself in her writing. Proudly I raised my head, yes, I too, was party to this success!

As Mummy signed her books, she frequently removed me from the chalet and held me close so that people could meet me. Unnerved by the experience, I allowed myself to be subjected to such exposure...Why?

Because I felt completely safe within the sanctuary of this little haven.

The day passed for me in what appeared to be a blur; all the welcomed attention had taken its toll somewhat and once home, with little reprieve, there was more fuss and attention as the brood greeted us excitedly, anxious to know all about today's events.

True to our promise, not a word was mentioned over Peanuts little outburst, not at first anyway.

"How many books were sold?" Thor asked whilst entwined with Princess Warrior Zena.

"Lots and lots!" I replied, supressing a yawn. I'd taken my usual position on the cat tree. "Mummy said it will make lots of pennies for the furries at the Rescue."

Magic stirred from his sleep, "So the books did well then eh Jack?"

"They did. There were lots and lots of people there, nice people who really cared about cats."

"Incredible. I'm proud of you lad." Magic's tone was full of admiration.

"I didn't write it though did I." I felt such praise was unjustified.
"No, but Mummy told the story for you, your story Jack, your little journey so far. Be proud of that. Be proud that this book will raise money for the rescue through you. For each and every book sold, that's money to help those like us who are less fortunate. Your legacy, little fella. That's surely something to feel proud of."

"I guess so." I replied, taking comfort in the fact that other cats and kittens would benefit from the additional funds the book would provide for the Rescue.

Peanut suddenly bolted into the room clumsily, grasping his opportunity to intervene, "It was UNBELIEVABLE! Guys, the paparazzi were all over me. Flashlights surrounded me and cameras clicked as the crowd couldn't wait to catch a glimpse of the infamous Peanut. Wow! It was awesome! Obviously, such posing was tiresome but..."

"You lying little shit!" Holly's impulsive and shrill outburst silenced the room.

"LANGUAGE!" Jasper admonished disapprovingly.

"Holly!" Shocked with her betrayal, I batted her with my paw.
"But..."

"Yes, you did well Peanut. Of course, everyone couldn't wait to see you." I defended as his posture wilted into an embarrassing slump.

"Scared..." Holly began but again was silenced by a swift ginger paw.

"I think someone's not telling the truth." Simba's voice was laced with sarcasm.

"I SO am!" Peanut lied.

"I think we need to draw a line under the subject. People obviously would have been excited to see you Peanut, the infamous squirrel face," Jasper tactfully defended.

"Lots of Cimicat paid for then, for the furries." Thor changed the subject as he groomed himself with his sandpaper tongue, sensing Peanuts profuse embarrassment.

"What cat?" I quizzed.

"You know, the formula used to feed kittens who need supplementing."

"I see." I paused, "Is that the stuff you had when you was a baby? Tell me about your journey." I couldn't quite ever imagine the incredible Thor as a tiny kitten with his fluffy Maincoon characterstics and his swishing belly.

"My mummy was a stray who had been sleeping in a scrap car in the garage next to the Rescue. Merlin, the man who ran the business couldn't get close to her. Mummy Hanes contacted a man called John from Cats Protection League and together they set up a trap."

"That's cruel." I grimaced.

"It's not," Tiddles intervened from her bed below. "Sometimes it's the only way of helping cats that are a bit scared and difficult to catch."

"My mummy was heavily pregnant so she ended up here at the Hanes Maternity Pad. Bonnie, Mummy Davina called her because of her fine looks. I was one of seven within the litter and needless to say with such a large litter, Bonnie's milk became somewhat depleted. As a result, Mummy Davina had no option other than to bottle feed us with the Cimicat. I ended up being here through default really." He mused, "But something's in life are just meant to be."

"Default?" My ears pricked curiously. I could never imagine Thor's presence within the brood being accidental...Mummy was clearly besotted with him and him with Mummy alike, they shared a somewhat very special bond.

"Well, one of my siblings was a cute black fluffy thing. It was always going to be him or me Mummy adopted but with her love of black cats she was drawn to the little tinker. We were all such a friendly bunch of kitties and loved Mummy Davina; she'd become our main food source after all. The week before our rehome date, Mummy tried to integrate the little one with her own brood..."

"...I remember!" Tiddles intervened, "Bloody spitfire he was too! Took a right swipe at me," she exclaimed, revealing her splendid fangs. "Not even these bad boys deterred him."

"My calling card," Thor purred. "Mummy decided I must be the one and when it was my turn to integrate, well, I made sure I socialised well enough to impress."

"You always impress..." Zena said dreamily.

"Take your romancing somewhere else, both of you!" Simba muttered disdainfully from the far end of the room. I'd not realised the destroyer was present until this moment. "Disgusting," he continued shaking his head.

Thor and Zena certainly did share a unique bond, which went without question. Both were frequently mistaken as siblings with their similarities in appearance. Holly once described their long-haired tabby characteristics to me in fine detail, as always, she was my vision in life.

The sofa dipped as Thor repositioned himself, he lay back, like a sheepskin rug, to enjoy the last rays of evening sunshine as the warmth permeated through the glass.

"Things weren't quite as straightforward for me during MY first couple of weeks here," Zena frowned, grasping the opportunity to disseminate her own experiences. "Other than Thor, the others treated me with initial hostility."

"Not intentional," Tiddles explained. "No offence but, you know, you had that smell.."

"...What smell?" Zena snapped.

"Well, sickness."

"Hardly suprising with what I'd been through." Zena pouted.

"You were abandoned outside like me weren't you Zena?" I asked, sensing her hurt; understanding that poignant feeling of rejection only too well from my own harrowing beginnings.

"A few weeks old, that's all I was," Zena grimaced. "Too young and far too small to rehome even. They turfed me out like a piece of rubbish and left me in the pouring rain. Alone and afraid I was, so very afraid. I can recall to this day that horrendous gut wrenching feeling of hunger."

"I've had my share of problems in life, but I can honestly concede I've never experienced THAT problem, must have been terrible feeling such hunger like that dear girl." Grandpa Jasper intervened from the solace of his bed, his sympathy profound.

"Matted fur and gunky infected eyes I had. Mummy Davina always says it was the angels who led me to the right garden that night."

"So, a bit like me, you had a rescuer?" I asked, more intrigued than ever.

"I certainly did Jack. It was a lady called Joanne who took me under her wing; she brought me in from the cold and fed me. The following morning, she took me to Oldham Cats Rescue."

"Surely someone would have fallen in love with you with your fine looks? I'm a tad confused as to why you ended up here," Jasper quizzed.

"There were no cages available and it just happened to be Mummy's shift," Zena recalled. "Thor became my mentor, a bit like Holly with you Jack. We've never lost our special bond have we, Thor?"

Zena nudged the now snoring Thor with her face emphatically, forcefully even, to seek his approval.

"Umm yeah, anything you say," he grumbled sleepily.

"Joanne calls herself my other mummy; still visits me she does. I mean a lot to her." Zena's unmistakable smile could be heard through her voice.

"Have I met her?" I asked, trying to recall the friends and family who frequently visited the Hanes residence.

"Of course, you have Jack. The lady who comes and sprinkles Dreamies over the floor."

"All the ladies sprinkle Dreamies all over the floor for us; Auntie Shell, Erica, Bev, Faye, Barbara..." I pondered, confused somewhat.

"The one that always makes a fuss of ME," Zena prompted.

"Oh THAT one!" I exclaimed, recalling her voice. "You must be special to her given she still visits. She must be an angel."

"And you have your very own special angel in life, don't you my dear boy?" More of a rhetorical question from Jasper.

My very own angel...
Indeed, I did have.

Jack and Jill

Following my initial and somewhat petrifying encounter at the Rescue, I do believe many angels have watched over me; continue to watch over me still and these angels do indeed present themselves in all shapes and forms. I'm testimony to this.

My incredible supporters have followed me from the onset, helping with my veterinary costs, following my journey and sponsoring my book even; the volunteers at the Rescue have expressed none other than love towards me throughout and the veterinary practitioners have aided and supported me phenomenally.

Mummy and Daddy proved to be angels in a very unique capacity...with love, determination and commitment; they'd become a pivotal turning point in my life. My future; my everything; my special world.

But one particular angel prevailed, one special angel indeed.
Her name was Jill.

A short while after my existence hit social media, a lady contacted Mummy from the Facebook Group. I overheard Mummy discussing this with Daddy.

"A lovely lady has messaged me asking about Little Jack. She's asked if we would object to her sending our little man a few treats."

"That's very kind of her. Haven't supporters raised over and above already, to help support Jack's operation?" he responded whilst engaging in a game of fetch and catch with me.

My sparkly balls, there was just something special about them and when Daddy launched one, I'd retrieve it and return it to him like it was a trophy. Mummy would play this game with me also but she was a bit useless in comparison to Daddy. I'd much rather play these particular games with my Daddy.

Immersed in play, I continued to listen into their conversation. "Darren will you listen to what I'm saying and concentrate!" Mummy snapped, her tone underlined with impatience.

Daddy averted his attention to Mummy, not before a swift under throw, which spiralled my sparkly ball into the air. With my extra predatory sense of sound, I listened on carefully, waiting for its impact with the floor.

"The lady has asked if we would object if she bought Jack a couple of sensory toys to help him some."

"A lovely idea. Do you know the lady? I mean, what an incredibly kind gesture."

"We've communicated a few times, yes. She's a lovely lady. She doesn't live locally but she's followed Little Jack from the onset...and well, she really does feel connected somehow with him, with what he's been through. She's suffers to some degree with her own health issues and there's something about him and his struggles that's really touched her."

I listened on in awe, my sparkly ball had now paled into insignificance somewhat. I'd really touched someone so much? She wanted to send me a gift because she cared? I chirped excitedly as I sought out Holly in the conservatory, eager to share the news.

Little did I know, at this point, the profound difference Auntie Jill would make to my life with her incredible love and care, her heartfelt gifts and magical parcels.

My first ever parcel delivered to the Rescue was addressed to Mr Jack Hanes. Holly and I were cocooned together in our cage when Mummy presented me with the package.

"Here you go little one. This is one very special little gift for you." Mummy smiled and nudged the package nearer.

Samantha (the Saturday chicken feeder) loomed over Mummy, frowning, "Aren't you going to at least open it for him?"

"No, let's see if he can manage it himself. All part of the fun eh, Jack?"

Holly, now alert, twitched her whiskers curiously, "Go on Jack!" she prompted.

Inquisitively I slowly approached the crinkly paper parcel. My predatory nostrils did a thorough sweep of the item, pausing now and then as the subtle scent of dogs permeated my senses.

"So, Jill has dogs," I murmured and gently penetrated the wrapping with my claw.

"Ooooohhhh! This is exciting Jack!" Holly rubbed her paws together in awe.

Enjoying the texture, I excitedly proceeded to claw into the wrapping, using my teeth every now and then to puncture and tear the paper.

"Good boy!" Mummy stroked me proudly whilst my audience of volunteers echoed words of praise and encouragement.

Eagerly I batted the strewn paper out of the way to investigate the contents.

"Wow!" Holly took a deep elated breath. "Wow Jack! Lots of bright beautiful toys!"

Indifferent to the colours, it was the scents, textures and noises from these incredible toys that intrigued me. Enthusiastically and with eager paws, I scooped out the sensory toys whilst I flipped, chewed, pawed, pounced and clawed inquisitively.

These toys were unlike anything I'd ever experienced; there was something quite unique and special about these interactive objects which captivated me.

Pausing, I sniffed a little further.

"Holly, we even have Dreamies here!" I enthused and dragged the packets forward for her approval.

"Aaaaw just look at him!" Samantha exclaimed.

"He's in his element." Sue added.

Mummy's hand invaded our cage as I wrestled furiously with the Dreamie packets.

"Here, little fella...you have a special message here." Mummy withdrew the card and paused some. "Aaaaw Jack, how beautiful. Let me read you your message from Jill."

The hand-written card with an inspirational quote had Mummy overwhelmed some. I could tell by her indrawn breath and momentary silence.

"Oh, dear Lord, words meant from the heart..." Mummy whispered before she proceeded to read out the heartfelt and poignant words.

Pausing from my chaotic frolic with my newfound gifts I listened to the heart-warming message from Jill.

She cared, my story had moved her and she wanted to make a difference to my little life; help in any way she could. A humble lady; her words of courage were truly inspiring and her admiration permeated throughout the message.

Long ago I imagined my disfigurement to be grotesque; not any more though, every day Mummy and Daddy told me I was beautiful, special and courageous and the sentiment in Jill's message echoed such words.

A silent tear trickled aimlessly as I was overcome with her sincere kindness and admiration, more importantly, her words of love, strength and hope.

This special parcel was indeed one of many as each and every week which followed, a parcel was delivered to the Rescue addressed to myself. Each parcel varied in shape and size; some were soft, others hard, some small and some humongous in size.

"There you go love. Another one," the postman said to Faye on one occasion at the Rescue as he handed over a parcel. "The owner's certainly a popular man."

"The owner?" she replied, perplexed.

"Yeah, you know, Mr Jack Hanes. He is the owner of the Rescue, right?"

Faye laughed and proceeded to inform him about me; that Mr Jack Hanes was actually a cat.

"One popular little fella then." The postman shook his head in disbelief.

"He's an amazing little fella." Faye smiled.

Mummy said I had this effect on people. I seemed to make them smile, in whatever capacity, I seemed to leave a paw print on their hearts.

It went without saying, this is the effect I obviously had on my Auntie Jill Murfin.

Each and every parcel I received contained a special message. This I knew as Mummy read each and every one out to me.

What became more and more apparent to my humans was that I instinctively knew who these parcels were from and indeed that they were meant for me.

On the occasions Holly and I didn't accompany Mummy to the Rescue, I waited on in anticipation for her arrival home, knowing that on most occasions she would be laden with a parcel.

Before too long, the brood alike became all too aware of the regularity of my special packages and that they indeed contained magical things.

"Jeepers Jack! This one's a big one!" Pepper exclaimed enthusiastically as Mummy returned home one Saturday.

Curiously I sniffed and explored the box before clawing away at it with my usual precision.

"Look Davi, have you seen him?" Daddy called Mummy from the dining room. "He's not daft. He knows it's from Jill."

Mummy's footsteps approached, "Hey cheeky! That should have been for tomorrow!"

Ignoring her futile protest, I continued to tear and bite away at the packaging until I could unveil what was lurking inside.

"Crickey Jack!" Thor was somewhat aghast. "Un-bloody-believable!"

"LANGUAGE!" from Grandpa Jasper.

As usual, a curious crowd had appeared from behind me as the brood watched on in awe.

"He's only gone and got himself his very own fire engine!" Thor exclaimed.

Mummy lifted the subject from the box and positioned it in the conservatory to enable me to explore.

With profound excitement, I sniffed and pawed at my vehicle.

"Here Jack," Holly ambled forward and pounced into an opening in the fire engine. "This is what you do, you can play in it."

As usual, my guide Holly demonstrated with her usual agility.

Within minutes I'd conquered how to enter my magnificent new fire engine, one of numerous gadgets that kept me occupied on many an occasion.

The brood, ever so patient, surrounded me whilst I enjoyed my moment of glory as they were privy to the fact that they too would receive their opportunity to explore.

Sharing was never an ordeal for me, on the contrary the magical gadgets and toys Auntie Jill provided me aided my integration somewhat even further within a surreptitious brood.

How?

My feline friends were, alike, curiously excited when my parcels arrived, they would watch on in anticipation and often clamber and play in the empty boxes. They would share the delightful toys and play centres with me and on most occasions, they would educate me on how to use them and indeed access them.

That was what Aunty Jill would have wanted, her aim to provide me as much stimulation and fun as possible.

The toys and gadgets were beyond my wildest dreams, each and every one selected with precision, clarity, much thought and certainly a lot of love.

Squeeky, chirping toys; toys that moved; toys that teased and tantalised; toys full of cat nip; fluffy toys and crinkly toys even...they came in all shapes and sizes and the limit to Aunty Jill's love and kindness didn't quite stop there. Not at all.

My fire engine extended to that of a range of magnificent toys and within time I'd acquired my very own plane and tank even. The cat stretcher huts and hideaways kept us occupied for hours and despite the darkness that obliterated everything; I was living a life of fantasy and fun more than ever, with toys that enabled my imagination to run wild and toys that I could indeed explore and make use of.

Auntie Jill's emotive and heart felt special messages continued and Mummy would read these out to me each and every time. Some say that animals don't understand, don't ever be fooled nor underestimate how astute our furry little kind are.

A perceptive little chap I was and indeed when my parcels arrived I knew who they were from, when Mummy read my special messages aloud, I knew these were words spoken from the heart.

Mummy, when permissible, would try to save the parcels for what she called her 'Sunday morning furbaby fun event', time dedicated to playing with us all...not that Daddy and herself didn't play with us daily, not at all, but this was her agenda most Sunday mornings where she got reciprocal pleasure from watching us play.

Such events didn't always take place however as, on occasions, I took it upon myself to open the parcels prematurely. Many a Sunday morning Mummy came downstairs to discover toys and chewed empty Dreamie packets strewn across the lounge floor. I would raise my head proudly on such occasions and showed little remorse when Mummy and Daddy were left to sweep and tidy up the blanket of orchestrated chaos surrounding them.

I'd long since realised these parcels were from my Auntie Jill and the temptation was often too great to wait till Sunday morning.

"Jack, are you not somewhat intrigued to meet this special hooman?" Holly asked whilst she played in my tank one day. "You must wonder about her."

"It's strange… I feel she's around us everywhere really Holly with all what she's done and Mummy says she enquires about me several times a week too." I paused thoughtfully.

My Auntie Jill. My enigma. My angel. "I would love to meet her yes, and although I wouldn't be able to see her, I'd know who she was instantaneously, with my supersonic sense of smell. I'd be able to smell her German Shepherds."

"You saying she smells of dogs?" Simba intervened from the far corner of the conservatory. "Not a nice thing to say."

"No not at all." Defensively, I justified my comment by explaining how, with our perceptive sense of smell, we could scent almost anything; a bit like when Mummy returns from her frequent visits to the Rescue smelling of other fur babies.

I pondered ruefully then returned my attention to Holly with a frown, "It'll never happen though, Holly. Never. Mummy says she lives too far away."

How incredibly wrong I was…

It was a mandatory Saturday morning at the Rescue and as per usual Holly and I shared a cage when there was one vacant. Mummy's absence indicated she was immersed in her usual chores throughout the morning, as were the other volunteers. It had been a good three weeks since Holly and I had visited the Rescue so I did wonder why the visit today; that was until the moment the adult room outer door opened, then I just knew as I heard the alien footsteps approach.

My Auntie Jill.

"She's here," I whispered to Holly. "She's actually come to see me!"

Holly strained her neck some to peep out of our cage, " Are you sure it's her?"

"I know so. I can scent the Shepherds. Holly! She's really come!" I whispered excitedly.

"Well you're even more beautiful in real life, you ginger hunk." A soft voice spoke into our cage, then she turned and addressed her attention to someone else, "Just look at him Lindon." She exclaimed.

Aaaaw Lindon! Her husband whom she'd told me lots about in her messages. So, Lindon had come too.

Holly nudged me, "Go on then Little Jack, go and greet her. You've waited for this moment."

Hesitantly and nervous somewhat, I crept towards the front of the cage to greet my angel.

Mummy opened my cage and lifted me gently, allowing my Auntie Jill to stroke me. Purring, I welcomed the fuss and attention and savoured the cuddles she offered.

I listened on curiously as Mummy spoke with Auntie Jill and Lindon, raising my head proudly as I wanted to do nothing other than impress her.

"Jack, honestly! Hold your head right!" Holly hissed impatiently. "You look dysfunctional, like you've dislocated something! Just be yourself...you've no need to try and impress, your Auntie Jill loves you as you are. Just relax."

And that she did.

A surreal experience in which I was cocooned in love, I couldn't quite believe this precious moment was bestowed upon me. I'd finally met my angel. At long last, she was here.

How did one define my angel? Did she drip in splendour and wealth? Was she adorned with jewels and smell of fine perfume? Did she wear a halo? I patted her head curiously with my paw.

No, no halo surprisingly.

On the contrary to all the above my angel was similar to all the other angels I'd encountered in my tiny life...she was soft, gentle and kind in her demeanour. She was here because she cared.

I smiled all the way home that day, satiated somewhat... after all, it's not like you meet an angel every day.

Abandonment and the Nanny

Banging inconsiderately, Daddy was the perpetrator who disturbed my siesta one Sunday afternoon. With my usual curiosity, I scurried upstairs in an attempt to make some sense of what was going on.

"You're kidding, right?" Simba's disgruntled tone could be heard from the bedroom. "Every year they do this to us!"

"What's going on?" I asked walking further into the room.

CRASH!

My head-on collision with the unexpected, large, rectangular object on the floor startled me somewhat.

"THAT'S WHAT'S GOING ON!" Simba muttered, clearly peeved, "THAT is a suitcase. I'll tell you what I think of it." He jumped from the bed and on top of the object. With malicious intent, he then proceeded to squat and urinate over it. "There! See how they like that!"

I recoiled from the smell and indeed his foul mood.

"Well, that was a daft move!" Magic grimaced as he walked over to sniff the suitcase. "They're clearly going to know that it's you who did that."

Holly bounded into the room and with similar confusion to myself, asked the question that was on the tip of my tongue.

"What's a suitcase?"

"I'll tell you what a suitcase is Holly," replied Simba, "and are you listening to this too, precious Jack?"

I gulped, anticipating nervously what Simba was about to say next. He spoke with such consternation.

"It means they're going away for a holiday and leaving us all behind. Rather spend some time sunning themselves than be with us, they would."

My ears pricked backwards with trepidation.

"Stop putting the fear of God into them!" Magic chastised Simba. "You're only in a mood because you'll have to stay here from now onwards."

"What'll happen to us?" I whispered, not quite believing Mummy or Daddy would EVER do such a ghastly thing.

"Now, now! Don't be getting yourself worked up," Magic detected my concern. "WE young man, are going to have a blast! Them going on their jollies means we likewise go on ours."

"Where will we go?" Holly asked.

"WE are going to go to the Rescue." Zena answered enthusiastically.

"All in one cage?" I asked in disbelief.

"No, heck no! We'll all go in the chalets, the bigger ones. I can't wait!" Zena exclaimed. "Them volunteers always make such a fuss of us. It'll be cool Jack and Holly, seriously, you'll love it."

Magic bounced back onto the bed, claiming his usual spot. Beside him Countess Tiddula Tiddles snored. He nudged her awake.

"Hey! Looks like we're going back on our jollies to the Rescue. Just think…" he licked his lips thoughtfully, "…all that chicken we'll get from Sam on a Saturday morning and all the extra grooming from Faye. Can't wait! What do you say?"

Tiddles rolled over, exposing her rolls of blubber, "That'll do me."

"I don't get how they can even leave us?" I pouted. "Have we done something wrong? Will Mummy and Daddy be gone long?" All sorts of questions seemed to be jumbling around in my head erratically.

"It's not a punishment silly billy," Candy smiled. "It's just a little break for them and they'll only be gone for a few days." She turned her attention to Magic, "Oh dearest, I do hope we're put in the same chalet again."

"Ridiculous!" Simba grunted disdainfully before stomping out of the room. "You all get a holiday while I have to stay here...It's just not fair!"

Magic's tailed bristled defensively, "Nor was it fair when you bit Jasper on the ass the last time you shared a chalet!...Karma Simba, that's what it is, karma!"

Magic's indictment of Simba was incredibly stern.

Poor Simba, my heart wrenched a little for him, after all, it was almost as though he couldn't help his spontaneous little outbursts and now he was being persecuted for them.

The 'holiday' and Simba's upset perturbed me some for the remainder of the day, so, I did what I always did when I felt troubled...I sought out Grandpa Jasper.

"No, no, no little one. You have it all wrong..." Grandpa Jasper consoled me, "it's certainly no punishment for Simba. Simba will remain here at home with Treacle and myself...Mummy and Daddy know we'll all be far happier here. On the contrary, we'll be spoiled some in our own right as Cerys and Chanel will be returning home to stay with us. As for the holiday, it's nothing to concern yourself over, see it as a little adventure young man and enjoy it."

The house turned into a hive of disruptive activity during the forthcoming days; Chanel and Cerys arrived home (their belongings strewn all over the floor as usual); Mummy was constantly busying herself daily opening and closing two 'Simba—scented' suitcases and the brood were engrossed in their excited topic of conversation, anticipating who was sharing which chalet with whom at the Rescue.

Simba, quite dispassionate about the whole subject was somewhat in his own elated little bubble now that Cerys had returned home. He was seemingly relieved that he was able to remain here during the holiday and spend some serious pamper time with his special human.

Grandpa Jasper was likewise indifferent to the whirlwind of chaos and change within the home, the only emotive comment he made was, 'Thank goodness I don't have to endure the travelling in that carrier on this occasion. It's not good for the likes of me at my age, not at all. Gets the old ticker racing, it does."

"When will the holiday begin?" I asked.

"No one's quite sure...but it's a definite you'll certainly know about it on the day. Trust me, little one." Grandpa Jasper answered with certainty.

And indeed I did.

In fact I had an inclination the evening before as the foster babies from the Hanes Maternity Pad were ushered away by Mummy's friend; fleeces, food, Cimicat and litter in tow. The 'Simba-scented' suitcases Daddy carried downstairs and Mummy was occupied cramming as much as possible into luggage bags.

"Two suitcases you've got Davina! My week's clothing is squashed into my hand luggage! How many pairs of shoes do you think you can wear? Take some out, you're well over 20kg here," Daddy protested as he weighed the cases.

I sensed the time was near.

Morning arrived and our mandatory feeding regime was disrupted somewhat by the banging, clattering and clanging of cat carriers...ten of them to be precise. That was the moment realisation dawned that something big was going down.

Shortly after, in what appeared to be a frenzy of activity, Mummy and Daddy secured some of the reluctant brood into carriers and within no time they were escorted out of the house. The car engine indicated they had gone.

"What about us?" Confused, Holly jumped onto the window ledge and peered out of the window. "They've bloody well gone without us!"

"Give them chance," Treacle also gazed out of the window from her advantage point at the top of the wardrobe. "There's only so many cats you can fit into a small car."

Impatiently, Holly and I waited and before too long the parents returned to collect us.

"At least it appears we'll be together at the Rescue," I sighed my relief to Holly along the journey. Quietly we travelled and eventually the car drew to a halt.

"I'll take Jack and Holly...You take their suitcase please," Mummy directed Daddy.

"Suitcase?" I whispered to Holly.

There was a palpable silence. She seemed distracted.

"Umm J-Jack," she stammered, "this isn't the Rescue, it's um...someone's house."

Fear began to creep in...now it was becoming clear.

We were transported separately for a reason.

I shivered with the harsh and brutal reality of what was happening.

"Holly, they're getting rid of us. It all makes sense now," I gulped nervously. "That's why they've brought a suitcase...for all our belongings. They've had enough of us. What have we done to deserve this? I thought they loved us..."

"I can't believe they're doing this Jack." The mortification in Holly's quivering voice matched my own.

"I think it's this house," the devious Daddy spoke.

Miserably I cowered into the corner of my carrier. All those times I thought I'd won over Daddy's heart ...how wrong could one be! How very wrong. As for Mummy, well, she was the one

I had always had profound confidence in from day one; the one was who was besotted with me and had invested every living breath in me…and now, just simply abandoned.

Forlorn and disgusted, I shivered as I awaited the fate to be bestowed upon us.

Knock knock.

The door opened.

"Aaaaaw, here they are. C'mon in." the voice spoke.

"Crap Holly!" I inhaled a deep breath and my ears pricked backwards. "They really have given up on us!"

Holly subdued, was far too busy taking in our new surroundings as we were ushered up some stairs and into a room.

Mummy and Daddy released us from our carriers and opened our suitcase of goodies; they observed as we tentatively and cautiously explored and sniffed at the peculiar woman.

After some time, Mummy hugged us both lovingly, "You'll have a fantastic time here little ones. You will. Debs here will take good care of you."

And with that she was gone.

Just simply gone.

Their abandonment made me feel more alone than ever…

"Hey Jack….Come have some fun," Holly distracted me sometime later as she clawed and chewed away at the ornate wall transfer, lavishing in what she'd peeled off already. Holly the explorer seemed unperturbed. Me, I felt lost without my parents.

The Debs human entered the room and sat down, wafting a toy to grasp our attention. Curiously, I sniffed then sniffed some more with some recollection.

I knew this Debs, I knew her, couldn't quite put my paw on it though. Frustrated, my mind went into turmoil.

Then at last, the penny dropped!

She was the very Oldham Cats volunteer who collected me from the vets following the removal of my eye; the one who drove

me to Faye's house that very first evening and indeed the one who offered me Reiki and cuddles. A good woman was Debs.
Such comfort didn't detract from the loss of my Mummy and Daddy though. Yes, I knew we would be loved by the Debs....but how could Mummy and Daddy do this to us?
My world was shattered, completely and utterly crushed.

At some point during day two of us trashing Debs' room she entered with her phone. Nothing of an anomaly there for Debs; this person was fixated on the buzzing and vibrating little handset.
"Here little ones...Mummy and Daddy want to speak with you," She smiled.
My Mummy and Daddy?
Both Holly and I edged forward with predatory inquisition to the object she held.
"Hello babies." In unison Mummy and Daddy's voices boomed from the device.
"It's really them isn't it Holly?" I said, aghast.
"It is. I can see them. It really is. There's lots of sunshine behind them, spikey trees, blue skies and um...they've got red faces."
Holly absorbed everything.
We continued to listen in awe.
"We'll be home soon baby boy. I hope you're behaving for Nanny Debs." Daddy's voice bellowed and we listened on attentively as both continued to tell us how much they loved us, ensuring they would be home soon.
So, they were coming back; they were really coming home! And Debs was our Nanny.
"They're really coming home for us Holly!"
"They are!" she smiled.
 Later that evening Nanny Debs presented us with a parcel. Instantaneously I knew whom the parcel was from. It was from

my Auntie Jill. Tearing and ripping eagerly at the package, I knew there would be amazing treats inside.

"See Jack...even your Auntie Jill has still been thinking of you," Nanny Debs smiled.

Feeling much more at ease, Holly and I adopted the attitude we needed to make the most of our little holiday adventure. Debs spent much of her time in the room with us and when we weren't exploring with vigour, swinging from the curtains or playing with our toys, we would take solace from the comfort of her cuddles and strokes.

Reassuringly, Mummy and Daddy spoke to us almost daily, telling us how much they missed us.

The week passed quickly and when Mummy and Daddy finally arrived unannounced one morning, it was with a copious amount of elated purrs and head butts with which we greeted them.

"They look kind of funny," Holly giggled beneath her breath. "Their skin is kind of ginger looking, like you!"

Despite having so much entertainment with our Nanny Debs over the last few days, it was certainly a feeling of elation that washed over me knowing I had Mummy and Daddy back within my grasp. Their embellished welcome clearly indicated they had missed Holly and I terribly.

"In a way, I'm going to miss Nanny Debs, Holly." I was still purring.

"I think we'll be seeing more of her Jack, I really do. I'm sure there will be many more opportunities to come back here."

I hoped so, as special as the Rescue was, nothing compared to having your own personal Nanny in life.

The parents; I should have known better than to doubt Mummy and Daddy's repudiation. I shouldn't have even questioned their love and commitment to our furry brood. Not at all.

We were going home and that's all that mattered; finally, to be reunited with our colossal and diverse family. One thing I had missed, in particular, over the past few days was indeed Simba's cheeky antics!

Hypothetically, one would assume that after having a period away from my home setting, I would again become disorientated with my surroundings and indeed the layout of the home. This certainly wasn't the case to be as I had everything mapped out in my mind, everything. Mummy opened our carriers and we clambered out.

A herd of paws bounded along the hallway and upon approach it was with sniffs, purrs, head butts and licks to which we were greeted.

A prodigious welcome it was! One that reinforced how much we meant to one another.

"WHERE THE HECK HAVE YOU TWO BEEN? We've been worried sick!" Simba exclaimed.

I smiled. So, you see, he did have a heart after all.

"We've been to our Nanny's," I replied proudly.

"Bleeding Nora! First you have an Auntie, now a Nanny... never heard anything so ridiculous! Next, you'll be telling us you have a private tutor, maybe a chauffeur, or you're born into Royalty, or...I don't know...!" he shook his head in dismay and walked away.

Holly passed me in the hallway to join Grandpa Jasper in his bed; she'd no doubt missed him terribly over the past few days with his surplus cuddly layers of warmth. Their roaring purrs emanated the moment she joined him in his bed.

Candy bounded down the stairs excitedly, "Hey there Jack! Nice to see you back. WE had an awesome time at the rescue, got spoiled we did. Magic and I, well, we had a blast in the chalet. Simply amazing, wasn't it dear?" she brushed her tail past Magic seductively.

"Sure did," Magic said in his usual, apathetic tone. He then turned his attention to me, "Come now Little Jack, tell us some more about this Nanny you have."

Thor wafted his enormous tail at me eagerly as he brushed past, "Yeah, come along. Spill the beans...I'm more interested in how many Dreamies they've been feeding you. That tummy pouch of yours looks to have grown some within the week."

"And your ass has got even wider." I laughed; my cheek had long since earned me respect with Thor.

Obediently I followed him into the conservatory and the remainder of the day was subject to us sharing our fun-filled holiday frolics.

They say absence makes the heart grow fonder, indeed this was very true ...being back with my human and furry family certainly made me evaluate what was important in life.

Three words summed it up, in short, they were 'my absolute world'.

With the lack of sight many would think this would affect one's confidence and trust in people; not me. On the contrary, I thrived from meeting new humans and was exposed to situations, which certainly enabled me to do so.

An ubiquitous boy, that's what I was.

Mummy and Daddy's family and friends first and foremost; I welcomed anyone into the home and would be one of the first to greet them, chirping and chirruping.

I'd long since mastered the art of greeting visitors at the Rescue and felt such confidence in doing so. After all, I took comfort in the fact that Mummy and Daddy would never expose me to any situation that would bring harm.

My story had long since gone viral, my face a familiar pillar within the community and beyond.

Mummy and Daddy, a few days following our return home from our Nanny Debs' once again clambered Holly and I into cat carriers.

"What the heck is she up to now?" Holly grunted.

"I don't know," I sighed, "I really don't know." I lay back within the confines of my carrier passively, taking some solace in the fact that wherever she would be taking me, it would be to humans who cared.

We finally arrived at a place called a studio where there was a large expanse of space.

The photographer, Karl, was most accommodating. Holly and I were encouraged to roam freely and whilst Holly displayed some level of trepidation, I sauntered around, sniffing and scenting out my alien surroundings.

Click! Click! Click!

Familiar by now with the sound of the camera, I posed in that direction, raising my head for the man.

"I've been asked to photograph some things in my time but when you asked for a family portrait, I wasn't quite expecting cats!" Karl smiled. Throughout the remainder of the shoot, Holly and I reduced him to rolling on the floor mimicking cat noises; anything to capture our attention for that precious moment.

The shoot was again testimony to how trusting and poised I was when present amongst the company of humans.

My frequent visits to the Rescue always resulted in me being showered with affection from humans, whether they were volunteers or supporters of Oldham Cats.

My book 'The life of Little Jack' continued to sell well through Amazon, reaching as far as America and Australia; not quite a household name by any means, but I'd certainly established my own little fan club!

It provided small but regular revenue for the rescue and I took comfort in the fact that these pennies indeed were helping to care for the abandoned cats within our community. Mummy even created my own Facebook page 'Davina Collette Hanes' and 'Ginger Little Jack'. The community page was a pivotal resource in terms of helping cats find forever homes; cats that were still awaiting adoption at the Rescue.

So, I certainly did earn my keep!

It was during one visit to the Rescue that Holly and I eavesdropped into a conversation that took place between Mummy, Sylvia, Samantha and Sue.

"The consultant had told me the cancer is terminal," Sylvia's soft voice was quieter than usual.

"I'm going to go ahead with the chemotherapy though, it's worth a try and I'm being fitted for a new wig next week."

Holly and I listened on with grave sadness. Our Auntie Sylvia; so very poorly. Devastated was how we felt.

Despite the trauma, illness, worry and fear Sylvia must have been going through at that precise moment in time, the determination, positivity and love for life could be heard with every word she spoke.

"I'm going to take things easy some as I'm getting really tired at the moment and I've told the doctors I don't want to know how long I have left. I'm going to make the most of every day with Rod. Coming here helps, so I still want to come as much as I can. Seeing the cats really does me the world of good. It gives me a purpose."

Despite the horrific ordeal she was going through, she still took such sanctuary in visiting us all; she still showered us with love, affection and treats.

"Holly," I stammered, a lump at the back of my throat, "what does terminal mean?"

"It means Jack that sadly this terrible disease won't go away. It's incurable."

I couldn't relinquish Sylvia from my mind over the next few days, life seemed so unfair at times, so very brutal. Sylvia was one of the most gentle of souls, certainly undeserving of this horrendous illness that had inflicted itself upon her.

All I could do was pray similarly to her humans who would continually offer the unconditional love and support she deserved.

The Hanes Maternity Pad

From the onset, I discovered there was something more going on here within the Hanes household. The first moment I ever entered the abode I stumbled past an intriguing room...a room, which was out of bounds to all us.

From the sanctuary of the room all that could be heard was the sucking and frequent cries from new-born kittens. On other occasions, the thundering stampede of tiny paws could be heard as mischievous kittens rallied and relayed around the room.

My Mummy actually grew cats; that's what I believed for some time.

This was a room we'd long since accepted as a 'No admittance zone'. Mummy would systematically (at three monthly intervals) bring home either a heavily pregnant stray or a mum with her new-born babies. The more severe situations involved Mummy bringing home just the new-borns or young kittens with no mummy of their own in tow; Baby Barney, Bridget, Toffee and Pumpkin all victim to this and indeed Mummy's ruthless hand-rearing.

Needless to say, my Mummy spent many an hour as a recluse in that room, immersed in her activities; her aim to nurture the babies and care for the mummies prior to their rehome...and this was something we'd all become accustomed to and indeed accepted.

"I once spent many an hour basking in the sun in that room. No longer permitted though for the likes of us," Grandpa Jasper told me remorsefully. "Not to worry though dear boy. One must accept that Mummy is doing some special outreach work for others too. None of us would be here today other than for the Rescue."

And I agreed with my Grandpa Jasper. One mustn't deprive those little ones and their mummies in need of one room when we enjoyed the luxury of exploring the entire house.

Mummy didn't quite stop there though however, Cerys moving out to University was indeed an opportunity she grasped and within no time she had her daughter's bedroom banished from a bed; it was subsequently converted into a 'Mummy and Baby Room' filled with cat trees, toys, fleeces…and indeed kittens!

The dining room once empty from the little critters was sanitised and finally free for us to explore, and explore we did with glee and orchestrated chaos!

This was short term however, as when there was a litter requiring hand-rearing or indeed an overspill at the Rescue, Mummy sought out the opportunity to help.

Two litters; one in the bedroom, the other in the dining room, often resulted in the home being overtaken by anything up to twenty-eight cats at any one time.

One litter, in particular, Bella's litter whose babies were born July 15th, was indeed a litter who made a life changing difference to us all.

The more demanding of litters consumed more of Mummy's time and Bella's litter was certainly one that was privy to this.

Mummy would isolate herself for hours in that room, armoured with aprons, gloves, sanitise, fleeces, syringes and of course the Cimicat.

"No wonder the bloody Rescue is short of fleeces!" Faye complained to Mummy on more than one occasion.

But, Mummy was obsessively meticulous in relation to her clean fleeces and ensuring her cages were padded out appropriately. Not all litters were consistent with toileting and such occasions propelled the washing machine into a frenzy of hard labour and excessive hours!

"NO! I'm telling you Davi...NO! Jack was different. I told you he would be the last!" prepared indictment was present in Daddy's tone.

Candy and I listened on attentively as Mummy and Daddy debated one evening.

"C'mon Darren, she's special..."

"...Aaaw Davi, don't play that card with me, they're all special to you!" Daddy protested impatiently.

But Mummy was adamant.

"Darren, I've poured my heart into her with hand-rearing. I really didn't think she'd make it and..."

"...You've hand-reared hundreds! Just stop it! I've told you Jack is the last. He's what you call special."

"Cheeky sod!" Candy muttered under her breath, infuriated. "We're all special. If he's not careful, he may just end up with a scratch or two during the night."

"I don't think he means it like that," I defended my Daddy of course. "Sssshh Candy, who are they talking about anyway?"

"One of the babies in the dining room," Candy explained. "She's at it again Little Jack. Believe you me, we've been here before. How do you think we all ended up here, eh?"

"You mean she wants to keep one?"

"It's always the poorly ones, vulnerable ones or difficult ones she falls victim to... I'm telling you Little Jack, there's going to be some change around here." Candy twitched her whiskers indignantly; "I feel it in my bones. Maybe you won't be such a 'special' Little Jack for much longer, eh?" she said waspishly.

"It won't be like that, I'm sure," I mumbled quietly, "Mummy and Daddy love us all the same, they do."

It was almost as though I was trying to convince myself as apprehension began to creep in.

Mummy followed Daddy persistently through to the lounge.

"I've even given her a name...Bambi."

"Well you've no bloody right to! You're being ridiculous Davina!"

"I'm not letting her go…"

"…Do you realise we have more cats here than the Rescue at this moment in time Davina? And it's a pathetic name too!"

"That's it, we are so screwed!" Candy grimaced. "She's actually given her a name! She never names them unless she's intent on adopting them. And HE'S not impressed! Not at all. When he calls her 'Davina', oh my, that means he's cross. Very cross."

I gulped nervously; this sounded serious.

There was a palpable silence.

"You really think she's adamant, Candy?"

"She is that. Look at me as just one example…I arrived here through default. Heavily pregnant, semi feral and terrified I was when I first arrived at the rescue. A volunteer called Fran, after being fed by a Mrs. Miller for weeks, brought me in.

I climbed them office walls frantically in terror, even pooped myself I did. No human had ever got close to me, so boy did I give them the run around in the wilderness when they tried to catch me. Mummy brought me home to have my young and I ended up in that very room myself." Candy turned her head in the direction of the dining room. "I would growl, hiss and shake in fear and wouldn't let Mummy get close to me. I hid behind the cabinet."

"Why did you do that to Mummy when she was just trying to help?" I asked, confused.

"Fear my dear boy. Remember, I wasn't really used to these humans at all other than when they fed me. In an attempt to gain my trust Mummy then decided to move me into our conservatory. Persistent she was too; she spent several weeks on the floor getting nearer to me, coaxing me; finally I submitted and allowed her to stroke me."

"Why did Mummy want to keep you when you behaved like that to her?" I quizzed.

"Aaaaw Jack, it was simply terror and vulnerability at the beginning. I'd never belonged anywhere really and certainly wasn't used to human companionship. Bear in mind also, us pregnant Mums have all these hormones affecting how we feel and behave. Scrupulous, tenacious and relentless Mummy was indeed in her quest to gain my trust and within time I submitted, Jack. She became my entire world for the next few months, helping me with my babies. Once our special bond was formed, she didn't want to let me go, nor did I want to either."

"How did she manage that with Dad? How did she talk him round?" I whispered.

"I'm a labour of a love Jack; he adopted me for their Anniversary as a suprise...He knew what a milestone I'd overcome and he knew how much Mummy loved me," Candy said, fluttering her lashes, "And just look at me now; her special princess!"

And indeed, she was; she followed our Mummy everywhere and habitually draped herself over Mummy's knee every morning whilst she painted her face in the bathroom. More portentously, Mummy reciprocated such love.

Me? I would simply amuse myself swinging and gnawing at Mummy's boot-clad ankles...it was after all, the time of day that proceeded breakfast time and Mummy often needed a prompt reminder that our tummies were rumbling.

Candy's voice triggered me back to the present, "I'll need to go and warn the others!"

"Of what?" I asked.

"Of the new addition of course; believe me, Jack, prepare yourself. It's going to happen!" And with that she scrambled into the conservatory, her tail bristled .

More to prevailing issues though...The Baby Bambi.

On many occasion of late, I observed dispassionately as my Mummy shut herself away in that room.
Baby Bambi being the cause, no doubt.

Little Miss Candy, with her inestimable superior 'princess' tendencies, grasped the opportunity to share the news outbreak will her feline friends, in particular Magic Hanes, with whom she scurried around relentlessly, with the aim to impress.
"Hey, want to know the latest?" she gasped breathlessly after scampering into the conservatory.
Many pairs of eyes pivoted towards her; whiskers twitched and all ears became suddenly alert.
"She's grown another baby! I'm telling you...We're in for some change! Another one's going to be joining us! She's even named her!" Ever the drama queen, Candy pontificated as she reiterated the conversation we'd eavesdropped. She reached her desired objective when she had the broods full attention.
Yawning, Magic stirred from his rest, "No she won't Candy. Mummy promised Daddy, no more."
Candy butted Magic in a desperate, somewhat disgusted protest, "Mag! I'm telling you, she's coming...Mummy has even given her a name!...Bambi! And by all accounts she's beautiful and fluffy and..."
"Stop there!" Magic halted Candy impatiently. "Listen, you know you're my girl so stop the jealousy. This new furry won't change things, not at all."
"Well, I will protest!" Simba grimaced in disdain.
"You protest at everything! " Tiddles intervened bravely.
"As long as my Dreamie allowance isn't affected with another mouth to feed, I'm ok about it," Thor offered indifferently.
"Fluffy and pretty..." Zena pondered, "surely not as pretty as I?"
"Here we go again!" Max grunted.

"I think all those little ones should be given a chance," Holly stated. "I wouldn't be here without the hand-rearing I received, I'm in."

"Daddy won't back down." Magic said with indifference.

"You're kidding! He doesn't stand a chance against her. You know what she's like when she's on a mission. Sounds like her mind is made up to me!" from Thor.

"Fluffy..." Zena repeated herself subconsciously, immersed in thought. Evidently, she prided herself on her long mane and was incensed at the thought of any female competition.

"We'll be outnumbered by girls at this rate!" Simba protested.

The debate went on and on and Candy hurriedly brushed past me in her pursuit to share the news with Treacle and Pepper upstairs.

I grimaced.

"Don't show such consternation little man," Grandpa Jasper reprimanded from the corner of the room and indeed from the comfort of his bed. "Let's just pacify the woman; it's where her heart is. You, dear boy, take up such a large proportion of Mummy's heart you know, nothing will ever stop Mummy loving you any less, none of us for that matter...so stop the worrying, it's needless."

Grandpa Jasper was right, I knew this; he was always right. Despite anxieties, it seemed inevitable that another one would be joining our astronomical and somewhat diverse brood.

However, I anticipated our day of change with trepidation and uncertainty.

Spits and hisses and 'bottle-brush' kisses

A mundane Saturday morning it was as Mummy prepared for the Rescue, only on this occasion her cat carriers were not intended for Holly or me. She clattered and clambered into the dining room with them and reappeared a short time after accompanied with the sound of multiple wails and meows.

Mummy placed the carriers nearby the front door temporarily as Daddy and she did their usual round of bidding us all goodbye; predicted jargon spilling from their mouths.

Curiously, I strutted towards the carriers and sniffed some at the scent. An overprotective Mummy hissed precariously as I approached her young; I jumped back alarmed somewhat.

The next carrier proved less of a threat as upon approach a tiny inquisitive paw branched out, followed by another and another. Unperturbed, these inquisitive kitties just wanted out of their cage. I sniffed a little further, overwhelmed by their tiny size and was rudely interrupted by a boot clad Mummy.

"Come away Jack, c'mon, come and play with your toys."

With that, I was shunted away as Mummy, Daddy and the two furry filled cages made their escape from the home.

Silence.

Curiously I sniffed at the dining room door. Was this Bambi still lurking? I remained there for some time sniffing and listening attentively with my extra predatory hearing.

Nothing.

Nothing at all.

She'd gone; gone back to the Rescue. We were safe.

For once, I was the inquisitive and assertive one who had masterfully earned that right to report back to the brood. Elated somewhat with my findings, I ran upstairs with my usual ineptness, banging into the skirting board occasionally.

"Hey! News flash! Gather!" I was so excited to share my findings; so zealous!

"The Bambi baby has gone to the Rescue. She's not staying!" I purred my delight.

My triumph was reciprocated by an abundance of purrs, rubs and praise for my incredible detective work.

This felt like the best day ever! No impostor Baby Bambi in the midst and finally I was the one who had successfully pieced together the jigsaw; Little Jack the Private Investigator!

Hhhmm...

Now then, have you ever had that feeling when someone has burst 'your bubble'?

Well, things were certainly just about to get worse for me!

The front door key turned; Mummy and Daddy were home at last. We stampeded downstairs to welcome them with our usual affection come teatime; on this occasion, we were greeted by none other than chaos.

"Everything's sanitised in there, I'll take her through." Mummy spoke to Daddy as she rushed through the hallway and into the dining room with a heavily pregnant cat in a carrier.

Okay, not brilliant but I could handle that.

Until...

"Oh and Darren will you set up the cage for Bambi."

What the heck?

"Here we go!" chuckled Grandpa Jasper unperturbed as Daddy wrestled to assemble a large cage, crying kitten in tow.

I ambled forward and sniffed the cage; my cage it was. The very same cage they kept me in during my rehabilitation all those months ago. The cage I frequently escaped.

"What the blazes?" Simba prowled unscrupulously. "Oh Jack, you've got this so, so wrong. A private investigator you call yourself! You're no more use than a chocolate fireguard. Pathetic!" His disdain was evident in his tone.

He hissed at the entity in the small carrier and IT hissed back, more so fearsome.

An array of abusive and disappointed comments followed from a somewhat disgruntled and perplexed brood.

So, I'd messed up. I'd got this one so very wrong.

Bambi had come home with them and indeed they intended for her to stay!

Daddy continued to tamper with the cage and finally he inserted the 'thing' within its confines.

Mummy was still immersed in her duties in the 'Maternity Pad' as Zena entered the room cautiously; her back bristled.

"Fluffy and more colourful!" she almost spat the words, disgruntled.

"What does she look like?" I asked irritably, somewhat impatiently.

It was on such occasions I desperately wished my eyes worked so that I could see the wonder of colour and light, I wanted to see this Bambi for myself.

Thor circled the cage inquisitively, "Oh she's pretty alright! A real foxy little thing we have here! A fluffy tortie with the biggest 'bottle brush' tail you've ever seen Jack." He continued to circle the perimeter of her cage, clearly impressed, "Hhhmm...the most amazing whiskers ever."

He jumped back suddenly as she hissed and spat at him ferociously.

"So, we have a spitfire, eh?" he mused. "Need to throw this little pugilist in the ring with Simba. She'd give him a run for his Dreamies!"

Hesitantly, I approached the cage when suddenly a paw swiped me. Shocked, I recoiled with trepidation.

Magic pushed his way through the crowd that had suddenly assembled, the more superior boss, investigating the new kid on the block for himself.

"Well, you certainly got this one wrong didn't you, Little Jack," he pondered, although there was no malice to his tone, more like humour than anything. "It's pointless sulking, you'll just have to learn how to make friends."

Not again? I thought gloomily. I'd worked damned hard gaining the trust and respect from the others, it'd taken months of hard, tedious labour and now I was expected to…CRASH!

With his usual ineptness and lack of agility, Peanut clambered on top of the cage to peer inside. His futile hisses then attracted Little Man Max who likewise pounced on top of the cage.

"Now! Now! Give the poor girl some space," Grandpa Jasper said dispassionately. He'd now reluctantly airlifted himself from his bed and was approaching. Such dispassion was no doubt due to the fact that he felt he had to move his colossal frame, I thought.

"You're overwhelming her; just consider, and indeed remember, how daunting it must be for that tiny one with you all circling like sharks. The show is over! Now go." He pottered back to his bed muttering to himself, clearly appalled.

"Deary me! Some of you have been in this position yourselves…I would have thought you'd have known better. Expected better of you all, I did."

The crowd dispersed reluctantly leaving the THING more settled in the cage as I sat nearby in dismay.

Zena retreated to the conservatory, sulking jealously; her female pride obviously wounded.

Holly took residence beside Grandpa Jasper in his bed, clearly indifferent to the situation that presented itself and the others scarpered.

Again, Grandpa was right. I for one, certainly remembered my initial few days at the Hanes Residence and how I detested the confines of the cage, it's loneliness and the impending fear when presented with such an infinite brood. Those days were indeed challenging and confusing; one hated the solitude of the cage, yet on the contrary, one also rejoiced in its fortification at times.

Bravely I trotted over to the cage.

"Hey! It's going to be ok here," I consoled the furry little spitfire. Defensively she hissed in return.

I took a step back cautiously, "Well, um, anyway...I just want you to know that, you know, that everything's going to be fine. M-My name's Jack." I stammered.

She hissed again and I retreated another step.

Get a grip Jack! I scorned myself. Pathetic you are, allowing a tiny little thing like this reduce you to a quivering, stuttering wreck! Man up!

I took a determined step forward and raised my head assertively.

"Little Jack actually or you can otherwise call me Lion Heart; the latter is obviously testimony to the brave, ferocious being that I am."

The spitfire lunged forward; hissing as she threw herself at the bars. Her dishes clattered and rolled and I could only imagine the blanket of destruction she'd created with biscuits and water scattering her cage.

Holly giggled mischievously nearby, "Oh Jack! You're so funny. Lion Heart indeed!..."

Sometimes there was a name for girls like Holly, but being ever the gentleman I was, I dare not repeat my thoughts!

The slam of the dining room door distracted me and I turned my head suddenly as Mummy approached, fragranced in other new cat scents despite the fact she'd discarded her apron and gloves. I could still smell the pregnant newbie.
"Aaaaw little man, I knew you you'd love meeting Baby Bambi!" she praised, stroking my head.
I shuddered but managed to disguise my disdain. Goodness me, was this woman for real? Loved meeting her? This tiny bushy-tailed spitfire had reduced me to none other than a nervous wreck!
'She's bloody horrible', I felt like screaming but Jaspers previous wise words reigned me in some. I remembered how vulnerable I felt in this very position, more so, being blind.
"Hey Jack, it looks like you have another new buddy little fella! Aaaaw have you been sitting there patiently wanting to meet her, hey?" Mummy smiled.

No I'm sitting here because I'm frozen to the spot in fear you daft woman! Oh heck, sometimes these humans had no idea, no idea at all!

Disgusted, I proceeded through to the conservatory to join my much-loved playmates when Grandpa's words halted me in my tracks.
"Listen dear boy, this is normal, perfectly normal...All these emotions you're feeling, I mean. With us territorial creatures any new addition will cause understandable angst. Remember how SHE must be feeling, this dear little girl; all she ever knew beyond her own mummy and siblings, was Mummy Davina during all that hand-rearing. This is all alien to her too. Her Mummy and siblings are now rehomed and all she has is us. We

are indeed a colony in our own right here Jack and we need to support one another. Please remember this, little man. This is a home where no one ever steals 'anyone's thunder'. We're all together in this, believe me, and we should be appreciative of them crazy parents."

"Thank you, Grandpa," I whispered somewhat implicitly, taking into consideration his words of wisdom and support yet again. And again, I knew he was right.

The evening ahead proved to be a worse ordeal initially but I kept my inconsequential comments to myself. Whereas the others had the privilege to observe, I listened attentively to the chaos that unfolded from the protection of Daddy's lap.

When the bottle-tailed spitfire wasn't purring and kneading on Mummy's knee she would thunder around the room enthusiastically, her bushy tail swishing and dusting everything she passed.

She explored and investigated with vigour, unperturbed by her alien surroundings.

Instantaneously I knew when any of the brood dared to pass her with the ambush of hisses and spits.

I grasped the severity of the situation when even Simba the Destroyer fled in terror after she took an unexpected swipe at him, the manic vixen that she was!

"Bloody nutter!" he spat upon his ascent upstairs, "Bloody fruit loop!"

Oh dear, I smiled to myself defencelessly; Even Simba had finally met his match with this little spitfire!

This tiny, furry one was beginning to intrigue me however; more, so humour me.

With some reluctance, I decided I finally liked her. I liked her a lot. Why? Because of her strong and volatile nature, I suppose.

I went to bed with Mummy and Daddy that night, thinking about how vulnerable she must be feeling within the solitude of her cage downstairs, but understanding such confinement was for her own protection, a necessity for such a tiny thing. I remembered being confined to that very cage myself....

Words could never express the profound loneliness I felt back then; I wanted to belong so much, I had no one...With courage, effort and determination I was finally accepted within the brood but I had to play my part in this too. Hard labour it was indeed for me.

I snuggled somewhat restlessly against Mummy thinking of her; I couldn't mentor her, no not at all...a bit clumsy I was being blind so I certainly wasn't the best candidate. But surely, I could help in some way?

Baby Bambi...I liked her, I liked her spirit. Tomorrow would be a new day....And how could she fail to fall for my charms?

The bed dipped suddenly and the bed sheets ruffled. Magic circled a spot a few times before finding his usual position.

"Good grief! Little vixen if you ask me, is that one. All I did was walk past the cage and she had the nerve to growl like she wanted to devour me for her dinner." He sighed.

"Is the kitten integration always like this? You know... so difficult?" I whispered quietly, not wanting the spitfire to overhear our conversation from downstairs, nor indeed my vulnerability.

"Not usually." He shuffled unceremoniously, frustrated by Daddy's invasive feet beneath the duvet.

Me, I was fine, I had my regular spot at the foot of Mummy's side of the bed; more considerate, she would reposition her feet for me, ensuring I had sufficient space.

"It's usually us that face the new ones with hesitation," Treacle said indifferently from the top of the wardrobe, her belly swishing as she moved. "Not the other way around. Cheeky little thing if you ask me."

"You're a fine one to talk!" Magic grumbled.

Such indifference from Treacle was no doubt due to the fact that, over the years, she had cocooned herself in her own protective little bubble and rejoiced in the sanctuary and solitude of the bedroom.

Frustrated was how I felt at times, as the top of the wardrobe was an area I couldn't climb, nor explore.

Spoilt to some degree Treacle was; I mean, how many cats had their own bed, litter tray, food, water and toys on the top of a wardrobe! All she needed was her own tiara!

Despite her timorous nature, it must however be said that Treacle was by no means antisocial and would frequently share the beds with us. It was simply a case of her doing things on her own terms; a bit like the spitfire downstairs I guess.

"I don't get it," I once quizzed Candy, "why won't she ever play with me?"

"Difficult past no doubt, Jack. Being dumped in a box heavily pregnant during harsh weather conditions doesn't do a great deal for a girl's ego or her confidence. We'll never know either what Treacle was subject to before...she's not one to discuss her past. Considering her difficulties and the fact that she raised her babies brilliantly in the 'Hanes Maternity Pad', we can't deny her the comfort of the top of the wardrobe at times, that's her private space. As you know, she does immerse herself in play frequently and can get rather excited...but sometimes with catastrophic outcomes as we know."

"The need for crash helmets for Mummy and Daddy," I mused, remembering the occasions where they would be suddenly awoken from their dreamy catatonic state, victim to Treacle's claws. It wasn't uncommon for Treacle to pounce from the wardrobe during the quiet of the night and unintentionally land on their heads.

"Pointless losing sleep, little fella over the spitfire." Magic disrupted my train of thought, yawning. "Let's just see what tomorrow brings."
He was right. It was futile to tire and concern myself over one whom was probably snoring harmoniously at this present moment in time.
After further anticipation over what the next few days would bring, eventually I slept.

"Little madam, she is." Mummy said to Julie from Crown House Vets.
Julie had called to drop something off for Mummy. It was day four of tiresome integration with the spitfire.
Julie, remembering the litter well, smiled.
She had previously cared for the litter during one weekend whilst Mummy and Daddy were away. Julie, a cat crazy woman within her own right, was always more than obliging to provide a little outreach foster work on such occasions.
"Picked a right one there, didn't you?" Daddy intervened disdainfully. "Bambi! Huh! More like Rambo!"
"She'll settle," Julie encouraged.
"She's no choice," Mummy said, lifting the fluffy little piece of ammunition. "Do you hear that? You've no choice Bambi."
Purring away innocently, the spitfire exulted as always from the affection provided by Mummy. A Mummy's girl, that's what she was.
"She's not like that with me." Daddy scoffed, "Scarpers from me every time I approach her."
"I'm all she's really known," Mummy defended.
"Well if you want to stay here you'd better 'man-up' Rambo."
Daddy made an attempt to stroke her; she hissed in disgust.

Yes, four tedious days we had endured with the spitfire; even Simba for once was at a loss for words but it was finally on the evening of day four we witnessed a revelation.

The spitfire made her very first attempt to communicate with the brood and as always food was the mitigating factor.

"Dreamies anyone?" Daddy shook a bag and proceeded through to the conservatory where we all lounged lazily. The spitfire had staunchly taken my position on the sofa; unperturbed by us all on condition we all kept our distance.

She was undoubtedly relishing in her freedom beyond her cage, Mummy and Daddy would only allow her to join us during supervised periods.

The heavenly sound of the Dreamie bag rustling propelled us all into action and with gusto we circled his ankles with anticipation.

I waited patiently at the rear of the crowd; knowing my limitations it was futile trying to worm my way through the wriggling and impatient furries, this frequently resulted in me being bumped or batted. I knew I would certainly receive my own fair portion in good time.

A ruffle from the sofa behind indicated movement from the spitfire.

I turned my head sharply, ears pricked back, awaiting confrontation.

The warm breath that fanned my cheek indicated she was nearer than I thought; too near.

"What's happening? What are Dreamies?" she asked in a soft voice, sniffing attentively.

"Aaaahhh! So the spitfire speaks!"

"What did you call me?" the little voice oozing confidence, asked waspishly.

"I...um...just a slip of the tongue. 'Bambi' I meant."

She snorted indignantly and must have turned as her bottle-brush tail whipped me across the cheek.

"Hhhm. No, I've never had Dreamies," she continued to sniff inquisitively.

"You can have one of mine. Here try one." I flicked one of mine in her direction.

She crunched enthusiastically; licking her lips then suddenly steered forward to grasp another.

"No! No! It doesn't quite work like that!" The assertive 'Little Jack' stopped her in her tracks as I swiped her paw away forcefully with mine.

"It doesn't?"

"No! No! No!...You need to earn your respect around here, little lady. Treating people like you do ain't going to earn you many Dreamies at all. Be nice to them..." I indicated my head towards the brood who were immersed munching away at their own delicious offerings, "...and they may well share."

Proud of my authority, I questioned her further.

"You're under the age limit for these anyway, surely?"

"Well, I suppose a few won't hurt," her untenable tone indicated that she was seriously considering the implications here.

Little Jack had, at last, finally asserted some authority within the brood. I was beaming inside, but ensured I disguised my joy as not to flaw my cool demeanour.

"Really, with a lady's name like that, you need to start acting like one...hissing and spitting at us all the time won't earn you any friends around here," I advised, hoping not to offend.

She recoiled a little from the onslaught.

A strained silence followed.

"It's all...umm, well, it's all a bit overwhelming, that's all," she conceded embarrassed. "I've only ever known my Mummy, my siblings and Mummy Davina. There's so very much to take in. I know what you all call me; I'm not a spitfire at all. There's just so many of you and you're enormous."

"We've all been through things," I explained. "We're a good team, really, well, most of us." I cringed inadvertently, wondering how I could explain Simba's complex character. "You need to learn to make friends around here spitf...um, Bambi. I can help, I can."

She ambled back onto the sofa, within her safety barrier, before the brood suspected her approach.

I felt humiliated by my own initial revolt and humbled by her at this point; myself included; we'd all mocked her volatile nature. She was tiny-tot and indeed must have been feeling threatened by so many enormous cats within the home.

I scolded myself, my actions were inexcusable and similarly to them humans even in life, well, I should have known better. I shouldn't have been steered in with the influence from others, no; not at all.

Myself and myself alone were responsible for my own choices and indeed actions in life.

Bravely, I joined her on the sofa, although sensible enough to keep a wide berth just in the event of her taking a sneaky swipe at me.

"Hey! You can hang about with me. I can show you the ropes." I offered.

Silence.

"I guess so," she finally responded.

"I can teach you how to climb those cat trees; I can teach you how to get extra treats and chicken from them human parents; I can introduce you to the others, you know what I mean, I can be your personal coach..."

"...You look odd," she interrupted, her confusion genuine.

I flinched by her outburst.

"You've only one eye. Why've you only got one eye and why do you potter around differently from the others?"

I cleared my throat before even attempting an answer.

"Well, I'm blind; I can't see anything. In a ferocious battle, I was, as a kitten! Boy, you should have seen the other guy after I'd finished with him though. I..."

"Oh Jack, tell the truth!" I wasn't aware Holly had been eavesdropping until this point. Giggling, she diverted her attention to Bambi.

"He can't recall what happened to him really. Yes, he is blind and such an enigma...I guess he's a hero in his own right, but certainly not in the way he's just told it. He's wanting to impress you, watch it Bambi...he's rather a ladies' man!"

I gulped, relieved that my ginger fur concealed my somewhat reddened cheeks beneath.

Holly proceeded to introduce herself and her somewhat satirical intervention earned me no less respect from Baby Bambi, thank goodness.

Day four was the day I indeed found myself another special little friend.

Assertive mentoring

Buoyed with confidence, I fulfilled my end of the bargain with Baby Bambi and indeed I embarked on the very responsible role as her mentor.

Within days, she began to pursue me, imitating some of my behaviours. She would follow me up the cat tree and wrestle boisterously. She would, as advised, scrape her paws along the floor and decline her dinner when the aroma of chicken was present. She would likewise share our litter tray. Oh yes! She was learning the ropes…and fast!

"I don't like being in the cage on my own at night," she complained to me one afternoon, providing the usual foxy-lady baby pout, "I feel ever so lonely in there."

"I've been there Bambi, I know. It's done with the best of intentions though, just until Mummy and Daddy are confident you're independent enough to withstand the brood unsupervised."

"But I am!" she objected.

"Trust them. They'll know once you're ready. Come! Let me teach you a new trick!"

With that, she followed me eagerly as I bounded up the stairs somewhat maladroitly and then into the parents' bedroom.

"Just watch Bambi…I CAN SWING!"

"Not again!" Candy complained from the comfort of the bed where the more mature cats resided; she turned abruptly and hissed when the bottlebrush thundered behind me eagerly.

"Ignore her Bambi, she'll come around. Now watch!"

1.2.3…

I retreated enough with hind legs raised, thus enabling me to pounce substantially.

And with gusto, off I went!

Within seconds I had mounted and was swinging from the bedroom curtains. Twisting, swerving and clawing; I was proud to have reached the top, my hind legs dangling precariously. I turned around smiling proudly at my amazing accomplishment. "Isn't this just cool, Bambi!"

Only it wasn't Bambi's soft voice that praised me, but the wrath of Mummy's furious voice.

So, exalted in my moment of glory, I'd failed to hear her approach.

"GET DOWN FROM THERE RIGHT NOW JACK!"

Her scurried footsteps approached, panicked she was into a frenzy.

I turned back and smiled more, knowing the pint-sized woman couldn't reach me.

"Bambi, look how brave I am! Not even Mummy can stop me!"

"OH JACK! YOU GET DOWN RIGHT NOW!" Mummy demanded furiously, flailing her arms.

The sound of the curtain tearing propelled me further into action; giggling I clawed my way up to the highest point, the curtain pole making abrupt contact with my nose.

Okay, so maybe that wasn't a clever move I thought, flinching.

"I think Mummy's cross," Bambi frowned, "and how do you intend getting down?"

"Watch! It's easy," I giggled, "the best bit even."

I descended the curtains dexterously by latching on; clawing and wrapping myself in the somewhat shredded fabric. The curtains swung harmoniously along with my body and before too long my paws made subtle contact with the floor.

"COOL!" Bambi breathed in awe, clearly impressed.

"I dread to think what them neighbours opposite think Jack with your monkey-swinging tactics," Magic said, amused. "I tried it once back in the day. Sadly, the curtains nor the pole, nor even wall brackets for that matter, withstood my weight. The whole lot came tumbling down on me. Never attempted it again, I didn't." he then paused, "More to prevailing issues, what's your dodging skills like because SHE'S on the warpath!"

The SHE, being Mummy stamped towards me. Oh dear! She wasn't happy at all!

I dodged to the left, then to the right. BANG! My nose made contact with the cheval mirror. Shaking my head disdainfully, I pivoted and took refuge amongst the storage boxes beneath the bed.

Bambi likewise scurried under the bed to accompany me, her immense tail providing a useful feather duster as it brushed along the dust residue on the boxes.

"Jack, come out right now!" Mummy's head peeped under the bed; her arms were too short to reach me and her backside was far too large to be accommodated by the metal frame.

"This is fun Jack!" Bambi giggled.

"Isn't it just? I told you I'd show you the ropes. Wait and see what happens next? It gets better."

Daddy's voice diverted my attention momentarily.

"What are you doing on the floor Davi? And what's happened to the curtains again?"

Breathless and defeated, Mummy stood up. "What's happened to the curtains is Jack... again! He's lucky he's not fallen and hurt himself! Honestly!"

"He's a cat Davi, that's what cats do, you know. He's not daft."

"Oh shut-up!" muttered Mummy, irritated.

"Watch what happens now Bambi," I whispered, "this just goes to prove how obtuse these humans can be at times."

As predicted, Mummy walked over to her underwear drawer and after shuffling some, extracted a packet of Dreamies.

I say! What kind of crazy woman keeps Dreamies amongst her knickers!

"Here we go Bambi...."

Mummy sprinkled the contents of the bag onto the floor and eagerly Bambi and I scrambled out from beneath the bed.

"See, I told you...she's so predictable."

"So, we get rewarded in this house when we do things wrong?" Bambi said aghast before retrieving one of the square delights strewn over the floor.

"So, it seems. I mean she's a bit dense in that respect, fancy rewarding poor behaviour!" I munched away contently.

My feast was short-lived as Mummy air lifted me into her grasp and read me the riot act. I'd heard it all before of course…how she cared, how she worried, how I need to be careful and so on. Well I'm a bloody cat, woman! I felt like shouting. Cats climb, blind or not, cats climb!

"You fall for it every time Jack," Pepper teased, now enjoying my share of Dreamies. "She puts them there to coax you out, not to reward you."

I wriggled impatiently as right before me, my feasting opportunity was fading away.

Did Mummy's words stop me from climbing the curtains? No, on the contrary, I climbed them even more. My new trick and I climbed with vigour until those very curtains flip flapped to heaven, no longer fit for purpose.

Bambi's initial 'spitfire' attitude indeed earned her respect amongst the brood within no time and as proud as I was of my superior mentoring role, something more imperative took shape; this foxy little lady became a true friend to me.

Even on the many occasions I cuddled with Holly, Bambi would be close by me.

Much of the time she would mirror my behaviour and it was a certainty that when Mummy and Daddy arrived home from work, we would always be in the same room; inseparable is what we'd become.

"I think she's done Jack the world of good," Daddy observed as Bambi and I wrestled with one another on the bed. "I just wish she wouldn't be so hesitant of me."

The true reality was Bambi was without question a Mummy's girl; the few occasions she wasn't with her mighty ginger mentor, she would be with Mummy. When on her lap, her bottle-brush tail would drape over the armchair as she kneaded and suckled Mummy's clothing. As confident and buoyant as she was amongst the brood, she was indeed cautious with other humans and would frequently hide when friends visited the residence. Despite Daddy's love and acceptance of Bambi, she would regularly retreat upon his approach.

Obviously, the offer of chicken or Dreamies was an exception to this rule and Mummy would encourage Daddy to feed her these to help build a rapport.

"I wouldn't take it personal," Mummy stated. "It's probably because we built such a bond during all the hand-rearing when she was younger."

Thor was a tad smitten with my foxy lady and would rub his butt against her at every given opportunity, but my Bambi knew where her loyalties lay and despite her harmonious relationship with Thor, she would always gravitate towards me.

When I played, she would play with me; when I climbed she would follow; when I slept, she would spoon into me…and when I wasn't myself, she would distinguish my vulnerabilities. Maybe it was Bambi's own vulnerabilities teamed with mine which made us so unified.

Holly of course would still always have a special place in my heart; the free spirit that she was, she certainly wasn't insulted any by my close friendship with Bambi and we still shared our own special moments.

"You're not upset Holly? Jealous perhaps?" I quizzed as we both relaxed in the cat tree.

"No, not in the slightest," she smiled. "Remember what I said to you some time ago, that time when you sulked like a baby; it's important that we make new friends and learn from one another. Our amalgamated brood wouldn't be as compatible as it is if it wasn't for our ability to form new friendships. There's no need to worry Jack."

"A right womaniser, if you ask me…" Thor intervened. "Having the ladies to yourself, it's just not on. It's about time you shared a little of the eye candy with others, Jack. Greedy you are…keeping them to yourself." He puffed in displeasure from below. "The day you take my Zena from me though, well you won't know what's hit you."

Zena was indeed his special girl; little did I tell him we'd had many a rendezvous together!

Countess Tiddula Tiddles interceded somewhat dispassionately, "You're all for the young ones I see, Jack. Not much consideration given to the more mature lady, eh! With fangs like this, you don't know what you're missing!"

She rolled over yawning and as she did so her rolls of excessive fat wobbled. A contended, middle-aged girl with the most incredible fangs; Tiddles was a sweet, harmonious little soul. Her pearly white fangs, which she was so proud of, were indeed her trademark.

"Did you grow from the Hanes Maternity Pad too?" Bambi diverted the subject.

"Not at all. I was subject to unspeakable depravity. I was an emaciated pregnant stray roaming Mummy and Daddy's place of work." Tiddles patted her tummy with her paw, "I've gained extra layers since, mind. This is what happens sometimes after you have babies."

"Um…I think it's because you eat too much," Peanut commented with his usual attentiveness.

"What happened to your babies?" Bambi asked curiously.

"Sadly, they didn't make it," Tiddles sighed ruefully. "I was Mummy's first ever foster. All seven babies gradually passed away. Losing the last one was by far the worse as he'd survived to almost five weeks of age. A Sunday it was when he took a turn for the worse. Crown House Vets were shut so Mummy and Daddy drove furiously to the emergency vets. Sadly, it wasn't meant to be for my precious little boy."

A palpable silence before she continued.

"He had to be put to sleep due to renal failure. Mummy and Daddy were mortified as they'd both tried tirelessly with each and every one of my babies over the five-week period with syringing and hand-rearing. Upon reflection, I was in such a poor state of health and certainly wasn't well enough to rear my babies. The catastrophic event didn't end there though for Mummy and Daddy; they incurred a speeding fine whilst rushing us to the vets and then a parking fine for parking inappropriately outside the vets! After having endured so much, they decided to keep me, they'd grown to love me."

We all listened on, in awe.

"Did this not put Mummy off fostering with seven dead kittens?" I asked valiantly.

"No dear Jack, no. My horrific experience seemed to fuel her some. The loss affected them both. Daddy and she did everything they possibly could for my babies. As diligent as Mummy was, she was also naïve in those days and when I came into my horny seasonal state, being the caring Mummy she was, she rushed me to a nearby vet, fearing I'd had a stroke. The vets simply laughed at her."

So, it became apparent tonight that Tiddles was indeed the founder of the Hanes Maternity Pad, the one who had propelled Mummy and Daddy into a love for what they do. They'd acquired a passion for bringing new furry little ones into the world; their initial horrific ordeal spurring them on further.

Tiddles lowered her head, deep in thought and I sensed her profound feeling of loss. "They fought for my babies, they did. I just wasn't strong enough at the time. I know though that more babies will live on in their memory."

Sniffling, we listened on to such a testimony and Tiddles' journey took on a whole new meaning to us.

Bambi was bold enough to raise the forbidden question, "Has Mummy ever adopted any cat that's normal?"

Tiddles sharpened her fangs proudly and smiled, "Oh dear girl, I do believe we've all arrived here for a purpose. Call it fate. We've all had issues at some point. That's Mummy for you; falling victim to those most in need. She's a bit of a sucker for the vulnerable ones."

I smiled to myself...that was my Mummy all right.

An opportunity soon presented itself for our Rescue to take a representative to attend a local pet store event. The aim was to promote Oldham Cats and we certainly considered ourselves the best to be showcased!

La crème de la crème!

"Why don't you take Jack and Bambi?" Faye suggested one evening.

"I'm sure they won't object to representing our Rescue," Mummy agreed.

Needless to say, one Sunday lunchtime, Mummy and Daddy scooped both Bambi and I up and placed us into carriers.

"Will there be nice humans there?" Bambi asked tentatively.

"Of course. Mummy and Daddy won't subject us to any harm. Trust me."

Harnessed up and within the confines of a large crate that accommodated bedding, a litter tray, food and toys, we both showcased ourselves to members of the public as they passed by.

Followers and volunteers arrived for additional support, much to my surprise; Faye, Gill, Patsy, Fran, Helen and Erica but the finale of the day was when a very special visitor arrived unannounced. My Auntie Jill, my Angel, once again had taken me by surprise.

The event passed relatively quickly.

Bambi relished all the fuss made of her, appreciating all the attention. She was safe in the arms of volunteer Gill whom was adamant, anyone who wished for a stroke of the fluffy little thing, used hand gel.

Myself, I was under the safeguard of Mummy and Daddy and the attention I attracted was somewhat of a different kind.

Many showed an interest in the Rescue holistically, but the focal point appeared to be their curiosity in terms of my disfigured face.

"Can he see?"

"What happened to him?"

"Is he in pain?"

"Does he lead a normal life?"

The questions seemed relentless and I certainly wasn't insulted by the bold nature of them. No, not at all, as many of the enquiries were generated by children whom were accompanied by adults. This line of questioning certainly provided my Mummy and the volunteers the opportunity to educate people further on the importance of caring for animals. *'These young ones are our future'*, Mummy once said, *'It's important they're educated properly on how to care for and indeed handle animals.'*

I agreed, with my harrowing beginning in life, I knew only too well the necessity and the importance of humans treating our furry kind well.

Within the confines of our home once more, I praised Bambi, "Hey! You did well there, you should be proud of yourself, not fazed by all those people."

She fluttered her lashes coyly, "Why, thank you. You were right Jack. It wasn't bad at all. I actually made new friends."

I simply smiled.

As for Baby Bambi, well, our own inimitable friendship had certainly taken on a special form

...the once Spitfire had truly become my soul mate.

Rags to Riches

It was a typical November evening, 23rd to be precise, and I listened on attentively as the rain harmoniously danced and tapped against the window. I couldn't see the translucent crystals but I listened on in awe, nevertheless.

Our rumbling tummies were an indicator Mummy was due home from work.

I pulled mischievously at the curtains before bounding up them, grasping one last opportunity before she returned. Dangling proudly from the top I took great pleasure in puckering and clawing the fabric. We were on a new pair of course, the third pair actually. When would Mummy learn that it was a futile effort to keep them in pristine condition with my little fetish?

The sound of the key turning in the door propelled us all into a frenzy of excitement. Swiftly I dismounted the fabric to join the others as they congregated downstairs to greet Mummy.

She shuffled through the door, always laden with bags. Her first task as normal was to greet us and she carried her usual inventory throughout the house to ensure each and every one of us was well.

What proceeded was her usual routine; litter trays, sweeping and cleaning the floors and despite the fact we sought the opportunity to chase and play with the sweeping brush, she continued with vigour.

Feeding time usually followed but this evening she was summoned by the phone. What followed had me completely baffled as she rushed outside only to return with a large crate. Noisily, she dragged, banged and clanged as she went through to the dining room with the large object and subsequently busied herself in there for some time before even considering our empty, churning and rumbling tummies.

"Something big is going down! You mark my words." Pepper said disgruntled as a superlative queue of thirteen followed Mummy through to the kitchen.

Finally! She'd actually realised we were wasting away here!

Simba prowled the work surface, pacing up and down in his usual predatory manner. "They don't usually arrive during the evening." His tone was somewhat baffled.

Grandpa Jasper trotted into the kitchen, always the last to arrive. "It means only one thing; this one's no doubt an emergency!" he observed.

"You're kidding! Here we bloody go again!" Magic groaned, weaving through Simba and Max as all three cats stalked the worktop impatiently for Mummy to fill the dishes.

Bambi's vertical foxy tail brushed past me as she skidded into the kitchen, "What's going on?"

"Another pregnant mum or mum and babies are on the way. You'll see," Max answered self-assuredly.

We waited and nothing.

Then when Daddy arrived home, he scurried in with a pungent smelling carrier, leaving it in the hallway whilst ensuring the 'Hanes Maternity Pad" was prepared and fully operational.

I veered forward to the carrier inquisitively. What greeted me was a cat in a withdrawn, somewhat distressed state. The poignant smell of sickness and neglect overwhelmed me, leaving a putrid taste in my mouth. 'He' certainly wasn't a 'she' either I surmised with confusion.

Despite his tenuous, weak and neglected state; he mustered enough energy to hiss ferociously at me and such venom caused me to recoil. An audience of furries had now assembled to peer at the 'bad boy.'

"Good Lord!" a shocked whisper came from Holly over my shoulder. "He's grotesque; a bag of bones!"

Mummy's hurried footsteps approached and gently she shooed us away. She proceeded to open the carrier and lifted the limp, sickly and emaciated creature in her arms before disappearing into the dining room for what seemed like a lengthy period of time.

Despite the fact he was now secure in an isolated room, the putrid stench that emanated from him still lingered in the air.

"Now, now! I'm sure this is nothing to worry over," Grandpa Jasper consoled a somewhat confused brood. The harrowing smell of sickness and filth and the sight of the bony, balding flea ridden visitor had surely unearthed unease within us all.

The doorbell suddenly rang and Mummy exited the dining room to allow the person in.

A new unfamiliar voice it was.

"Thank you so much for this, really Davina. I've come to see how he is. We had to get him away from there and quick. We didn't know where else to go with him."

"Unspeakable depravity and neglect," Mummy's voice was grave, "come through you can see him. He'll have to go to the vets first thing in the morning, he's in a terrible state."

"Famished he is," Daddy interjected, his tone sinister. "Absolutely bloody starving! No animal should be subject to living like this."

All three humans shut themselves away into the dining room. Curiously, we eavesdropped but with muffled voices we could only pick out certain words; all of which depicted this poor soul had been subject to horrific beginnings.

In time, the visitor left and Mummy spent the remainder of the evening in the now 'Hanes Recovery Pad'.

The evening ahead was a disturbing one for us all; Mummy and Daddy sleepless over the poorly one, ourselves sleepless over the neglect he was subject to and indeed an unpredictable few weeks ahead. Should he survive, it was a sure thing that neither

the Rescue and its volunteers, nor Mummy and Daddy would give up on him.
One thing I did learn tonight was that Oliver was his name.

My routine visit at Crown House Vets the following morning resulted in me being accompanied by the sickly patient. The journey was tense; him in his carrier, me in mine.
Despite the repugnant smell that contaminated the car I held my nostrils and braved enough confidence to try to console him, "It'll be ok. Really it will, you'll get better."
He spat back at me incoherently, his already vulnerable and lethargic state shivering more from the added stress of the journey.
It was a new vet we saw; Ornella was her name. Within the confines of my carrier I listened on as she proceeded to thoroughly examine Oliver.
"Where he come from and history please?" she probed, her Argentinian Spanish accent accentuated.
I listened on with profound despondency as Mummy explained to the vet the circumstances he had been subjected to.
"Oh Oooo-liver! Poor baby boy, let's have a look at you... beautiful boy." The vet tried to comfort the limp cat as she further examined him. She shook her head with empathy, " Aaaaw, Oooo-liver how can this be, you poor, poor boy!"
After a thorough examination, she turned her attention to my parents.
"Extreme alopecia due to fleas," she stated as the blood sucking critters continued to feed from Oliver's gaunt body.
Daddy flinched, "Good God! I've never seen anything as big!"
"I've front-lined him but it's just not shifting them. He's had severe diarrhoea also, overnight. Very lethargic too," Mummy frowned.
"Hind paws very cold, severe dehydration, acute anaemia, this cat... Oooo-liver is very, very poorly. This is not good." The vet,

Ornella, continued to explain her intended strategy of treatment. "We will run bloods but he needs intravenous fluids straight away. This cat, not good, not good."
She stroked Oliver and he snarled and flinched as she made contact with his back.
"Aaaaw Oooo-liver, who did this to you, eh? Who hurt you, poorly boy?" She turned her attention back to Mummy and Daddy and pointed to Oliver's rear, "He, here, he been hurt here I think. Very sensitive."

I decided I liked this vet; it was gratifying to hear her speak with such sincere concern and affection for him. As she whisked Oliver away (Or Oooo-liver as she pronounced) I knew he was in good care with Crown House Vets. I knew they would all do everything possible to help him.
During my journey home, my heart tugged a little at the thought of leaving Oliver alone and on intravenous fluids; I remembered the feeling only too well during my own wretched periods of illness.
Silently I said a little prayer for him.

As ambivalent as I was over the invasive bony Oliver, his frail condition and his horrific past experiences had me deeply distraught. No animal should have to endure what he'd been subject to, no animal at all. It was with grave concern I relayed what had happened to the remainder of the brood.
"Poor, poor chap," Grandpa Jasper frowned. "Let's pray he mends well and eventually can find a special home at the Rescue."
It was with some sense of misguided relief that Oliver came home later during the evening and back into his isolated rehabilitation pad. Mummy spent most of the evening in there...I clawed at her door impatiently, feeling somewhat deprived of attention.

Magic sauntered past, as usual taking everything in his stride, "Leave her be in there, lad. Let her do what she needs to do." Feeling rejected some, I did what he advised.

It was much later Mummy came to bed, when her head finally hit the pillow she let out a troubled sigh.

I could sense her anxiety and it was some time before she drifted into a sleep.

So, what would tomorrow bring? I wondered apprehensively before nestling into the crook of her arm and drifting into my own deep sleep.

The events that unfolded for the next few days certainly were somewhat of a repetitive cycle. The bony Oliver visited the vets daily and much of Mummy's time was invested with him in his recovery pad. She would do her day's pittance at work, come home and tend to us all in her normal loving manner but then her time spent in that room with him was an indicator, things weren't improving.

"He's not eating much at all. He still has the runs too," Mummy complained to Daddy on the Thursday evening. "He seems so lethargic and frail."

"Give the medication time Davi, it's only been four days."

But by Friday evening his problematic symptoms had worsened some. The gut wrenching sound of projectile vomiting could be heard coming from the recovery pad. Needless to say Mummy remained in there all night.

The following morning Mummy and Daddy made an emergency appointment for Oliver at Crown House Vets; Mummy's day at the Rescue even forfeited.

"Do you think he'll be okay?" Bambi asked, her concern evident.

"All we can do is pray for him Bambi," I replied, not holding much hope myself.

For the remainder of the day, that's exactly what we did.

Later the parents arrived home without Oliver.

We feared the worse until we heard Mummy's conversation to Faye over the phone. Mummy sounded distraught and tired.

"We've had to rush Oliver up to Armac for emergency surgery."

A pause as Faye was obviously replying.

"Ornella examined him this morning and discovered a mass. She sounded concerned and said it wasn't there the day previous. She was upset even; I think she's developed a real soft spot for him. With the vets closing midday, Oliver's had to go to the out of hours emergency vets. We don't know yet what the cause is but they'll be operating straight away. I pray it's not a tumour. He doesn't deserve any of this in life, it's just not fair what he's been through," Mummy's voice wavered.

Another silence, a longer one.

My! That Faye could talk!

"Certainly. I'll let you know as soon as Armac phone me."

With that, Mummy put the phone down and sighed deeply as she slumped on the sofa.

Sensing she needed some cuddle therapy, I clambered onto her knee and rubbed my face against hers reassuringly. She stroked my face softly.

"Oh dear Jack! What a mess eh, little fella?" she murmured as she continued to stroke me.

Daddy approached, "Well, have they phoned yet over Oliver?" his voice was also threaded with grave concern.

"No. Nothing." Mummy mumbled despondently and diverted her attention back to me.

For the remainder of the day I latched onto Mummy and Daddy, sensing their anticipation, sensing their dull demeanour.

No truer word spoken in terms of how animals can send positive vibes and how their positive aura can provide therapy for humans. And this is exactly what I embarked on doing; anything to comfort them.

When Mummy's phone finally did ring, she ran (yes ran, which was somewhat of an anomaly) to the kitchen and grabbed it.

"Hello," she said breathlessly.

"Oh, thank God for that! Yes."

A silence followed for several minutes.

"So, it was a blockage in his duodenum. Sorry, can I just get a pen to write this down…"

Mummy snatched a pen from the work surface and began to scribble.

"He's still on a drip…Impacted food it was, dear God."

A further strained stillness.

"Overnight stay…Yes, yes, of course thank you."

Conversation finished, Mummy directed her attention to Daddy who had followed her.

"A blockage it was in his duodenum, an impactation of food in the pylorus area. He's got pancreatitis too now, possibly secondary due to the obstruction. He's still very lethargic and has diarrhoea so he's staying in overnight. We'll just have to see what tomorrow brings."

"Poor little bugger. What caused the blockage?" Daddy frowned.

"Probably that starved; he's not used to eating. He's going to be in a lot of pain with the pancreatitis too, they said. He'll need further close monitoring so he won't be going anywhere for a while. Once he's over this, we'll just have to concentrate on building him up some," Mummy sighed. "And again, the incredible support, love and donations from our Oldham Cats supporters has been so phenomenal, it simply can't be quantified in words alone. There are some incredible people out there Darren. He's surrounded in love and prayers, he really is. We'll get there."

Oliver arrived home the following day and for several days after he was subject to veterinary visits at Crown House Vets.

"He really wouldn't be here but for them. They've been incredible with him; they've monitored him ever so closely. He's even gaining weight now. and I feel that deprivation and sadness is going from his eyes. They don't have that haunted, scared look anymore...not quite a sparkle yet but we're getting there. He purrs now, it's as if he knows he's safe." Mummy told Daddy as she prepared Oliver's special prescription diet. "I just wish he wouldn't flinch when we touch that area of his back, something's definitely happened there."

My nose twitched, as I could smell Mummy prepare Oliver's chicken; clawing at her ankles and chirping impatiently, I reminded her of my hungry presence.

"Here, little fella," she bent down and after prizing my claws from her leggings, fed me some of the succulent meat.

"Bloody great, eh! We get 'Good as it Looks' when bony lad in there gets steamed chicken! An absolute joke if you ask me!" Simba snorted as he prowled the kitchen worktop.

"His coat's slowly growing too," Daddy acknowledged, "I just thank God we got to him just in time. Ornella said he would have been dead within the week. He's a little fighter."

Undeniably he was just that, no one could argue that point. Despite my own imperfections and blindness, humbled I felt sometimes, listening to Oliver's suffering and despicable neglect. No animal should be exposed and subject to what he had endured.

The next vet visit, I accompanied Oliver. Our carriers were in such close proximity in the rear of the car, they almost touched. My benevolent temperament urged me to try to make conversation.

"Umm, hey...A-are you feeling, um, better?"

Nothing.

I scrambled forward and extracted my paw towards him.

"Back off!" he spat vehemently. "Get any closer and you'll regret it!"

I flinched from his vulgar tone and the long list of explicit words that followed from him.

"That's really rude. I-I p-prayed for you, y-you know," I stammered, still recoiling from the vulgarities that escaped his mouth.

"Huh! Ya think a street cat like me needs ya prayers. Keep em! Looks like ya need em yourself lookin at that face!"

I gulped. Thankfully I'd long since developed enough confidence not to accept such insolence.

"These are war wounds, I'll have you know. Battle scars they are! I'm a fierce Lion Heart!"

Silence.

That got him thinking and for the duration of the journey we drove in quietness. For once, I'd actually stepped up to the mark!

Within the consultation room we were greeted by the Ornella vet.

"Oooohh, Oooo-liver, my baby boy, you're looking so good." She drawled and subject him to a thorough examination prior to weighing him.

"He's put on weight," she smiled. Clearly, this boy was special to her. I meowed in my carrier for some attention, she continued with Oliver however, his needs prevailing. I could hear the patter of paws as Oliver freely explored the consult room, lapping up the attention.

"He's doing well," Ornella informed the parents. "Still very depressed though, maybe he would benefit from a companion, you know, to teach him how to interact. After all, if he's never been shown love or good behaviour, he won't know how to reciprocate. Have you cats other than Jack?"

Mummy gulped, "A few."

"How many?" she asked placing Oliver back within his carrier.

"Umm…fourteen," Mummy replied.

Ornella paused, aghast.

"Oh my! I see…um… well, I still feel this boy needs to learn appropriate behaviour around others, you see. Try him! Maybe a home with other cats would be good for him. "

"YOU'RE KIDDING ME!" the bony boy hissed from within his carrier.

"NO WAY!" I gasped.

"He's suffered a level of depravity which denies belief. I'm just amazed with his progress," Mummy said proudly. "Thank you for all you've done. We'll see about trying him with the others but ultimately he will need rehoming," Mummy answered.

A synchronised 'PHEW!" emanated from our carriers.

"Why don't you have him?" Daddy asked the vet. "You've obviously got a soft spot."

My whiskers twitched in hope.

The vet laughed, "No, no…I cannot where I live."

I sighed despondently. Good on Daddy though! It was worth a try.

Back home we went with the bony, precarious Oliver in tow.

The street Cat

The stench of vomit and diarrhoea had long since dissipated from the recovery pad so why, we wondered, in God's name, was Oliver still here when Mummy said he would need rehoming?
She had even put out a rehome appeal...and nothing.
It was now December, he had been here weeks and there was absolutely no sign of Oliver going back to the Rescue.
"I know he's had it rough, but this seems to be going on and on doesn't this? I'd rather hear screaming babies in that room as opposed to his sickly male dominance," Simba frowned, sniffing the doorway.
"I don't care anymore. I'm going in! Take your positions all!" and with a forceful manoeuvre he forced the door ajar...a skill he had long since mastered.

The door creaked open and inquisitively, like an army almost, we crept into the recovery pad. Unperturbed by our presence and indeed our probing, Oliver, our subject, lay there motionless in a cat bed on top of the dining room table.
He turned his head once, only once, then curled back into a ball. With predatory inquisitiveness, we crept forward, almost in slow motion as if we were stalking our prey.
"What can you see?" I whispered to Tiddles.
"He's just lay there, skinny looking thing," she replied.
Simba and Max fearlessly pounced on the table top and sat there. I awaited a ferocious attack, a fierce battle to begin...but nothing.
So, intrigued, we were oblivious to Mummy arriving home from work.
"What the bloody hell?...Goodness me! OUT!" Confounded, she gasped.
Crap! Caught red handed, the lot of us.

Whilst she focussed on removing the more insubordinate furries, I scurried between her feet and followed Holly as she bounded upstairs. I listened on for a further ten minutes as Mummy crawled along the dining room floor, frantically trying to catch Max, Simba and Pepper who evidently decided to play 'cat and mouse' with her.

"Bit of a push-over if you ask me," Simba stated a short while after. "Didn't even flinch when we went in."
"He has a foul mouth though," I warned. "Remember, I've had first-hand experience with him. Street-wise, that's what he is."

But it was Mummy who really triggered the alarm bells later that very evening.
Horrified and with ears pricked, we listened on as Mummy spoke to Daddy.

"We may as well just leave the door open Darren. Look at him; he's so depressed. Honestly, when Simba opened the door earlier, most of the cats went into the room. There wasn't any antagonism. I think the vet was right, we need to give him a chance at least."
"Fine then…. but you do know we won't be keeping him, Davi. I said no more after Jack and look what happened!" Daddy's stern voice was full of rebuke. "But he's welcome to stay as long as he needs to and I mean that. He needs us right now."
"You bloody fool!" Magic reprimanded Simba with a swift bat of his paw. "This is your sodding fault…AGAIN!"
"Why me?" Simba jumped back, startled.
"If you hadn't have opened the door earlier then we wouldn't be in this mess!" Magic hissed furiously. "You've really planted the seed for Mummy. Well, I'll tell you what Simba…In life, you reap what you sow, judging from what Little Jack has said; you've certainly met your match this time pal!"

A palpable silence followed, after which, the Destroyer grunted, "Well, you can't squeeze the toothpaste back in the tube, can you? It's pointless moaning about it NOW."

"What are we in for?" I whispered in dismay.

"Wait and see. Just you wait and see," Magic replied with such potency. "He's weak and recuperating at present, hence his dormant state. Mark my words though boy...the beast will soon come to life."

The Recovery Pad door was indeed left open that night and we all explored apprehensively; prowling, hissing and spitting...we did what we did best as predators, but to no avail, bony Oliver simply lay there unresponsive.

This was soon about to change.

Several days later we entered the room confidently with the same determination and state of inquisition. Max pounced on the table-top to seek out Oliver's gourmet chicken meal but a startled Oliver unexpectedly roared to life and took a harsh swipe at him.

We were affronted by a series of hisses as he lashed out, muttering a string of obscenities in the process.

A foul mouth he had, that was for sure.

Simba the Destoyer confronted him, back bristled, confident in his demeanour...only to be cornered by the fearsome perpetrator.

They glared at one another fiercely, neither cat prepared to be conquered.

Their siege, only lasting seconds seemed endless, fuelled with such hostility and male territorial determination.

I scurried back through the doorway, fearful at this point. Indecisive of what would happen next, I needed to armour myself, protect myself against both tyrants. Never had I witnessed hostility like it...so I took refuge behind Magic's solid frame.

After spits, hisses and futile clawing, both villains finally dissipated. Simba, somewhat defeated, retreated upstairs; Oliver back in his bed.

This was only the first of a series of spats between the two dominant males.

The dining room door remained open and curiously we would still intrusively enter.

Oliver remained impassively quiet within the confines of his blue, fluffy bed which he loved. The blue bed was initially mine; a gift from my angel Jill Murfin, but I kindly loaned it to him. He was clearly in more need than I.

He took such sanctuary in this bed, that eventually Mummy decided to let him keep it. He'd probably never experienced the warmth and comfort of a bed before.

Yes, he would watch on wearily as we pottered around the perimeter of the dining room, never speaking, just watching. Though, cautious as he was, he appeared somewhat unperturbed by our presence. It was however, a different story on the occasions when one got within too close a range of him. Such times would propel him into lashing out and indeed there were many a hostile confrontation between him, Simba and Max. With each conflict, the initiator and main perpetrator was always Oliver and despite his selective mutism, he wouldn't think twice about growling sordid, ghastly obscenities at them. "We're all trying our best with him," disconcerted, I complained miserably to Grandpa Jasper one day. "But he's just not being nice at all to any of us. I wouldn't mind, I even donated my favourite bed to him from Auntie Jill. He's not helping himself...I just don't understand."

And that's exactly what was disturbing me.

Yes, I was certainly privy to experiencing resilient hostility from the brood back in the day, but Oliver's anti-social and aggressive temperament was something completely on a different scale. True to Magic's word, even Simba had finally met his match with, 'street cat'.

"I think, dear boy, you're overthinking this. Remember how vulnerable you felt at first. You need to put yourself in Oliver's position, that boy has had an incredibly grim time of previous. He's damaged goods so to speak and through encouragement and caring behaviours from yourselves, I have every confidence he will improve in time," Grandpa Jasper said candidly. "You chaps bulldozing your way in there after what he's been through will certainly overwhelm the poor soul. Far too much for him to comprehend...of course he will panic!"

I absorbed what Grandpa Jasper was telling me. He was right yet again, I surmised.

"He should have bloody well gone back to the Rescue long ago if you ask me! I can't even begin to imagine what that woman was thinking bringing a low-life like him into the home," Simba spat in disgust as he pushed past me.

"Back to the Rescue Simba?" Grandpa Jasper taunted. "We shall see... we shall see."

"You seriously don't think so?" I gasped in dismay.

"No dear boy, I doubt it very much. It doesn't hurt to get Simba wondering though, now does it? This one is quite a challenge and Mummy has enough on at present."

Hypothetically, Grandpa was right but the significant amount of time and effort Mummy was pouring into Oliver, well, one couldn't help but wonder.

I did nevertheless trust Grandpa's judgement so therefore continued on with my playful antics, much more pacified.

Days however, evolved into weeks and Mummy one evening dropped the 'bomb shell' to Daddy that I was dreading.

"I'm thrilled Oliver's eating much better and he's gained so much weight. I would still recommend though he needs feeding up some Darren so it's a certainty he'll be staying over Christmas."

"I agree. We need him completely right before he's rehomed."

"What's Christmas?" I whispered to Zena as she sat beside me from the comfort of the sofa.

"It's a fabulous season...a time where the bearded man wearing red and white brings us lots of presents. It'll be your first, Jack, you'll just love it. There are lots of twinkly lights, a tree we can climb in and delicious food. Anyway sshhh! Listen..."

"I think he's struggling in that room, he's just not moving or pottering about so I think he can have the study," Mummy suggested.

"That's fine but you do realise, as much as he breaks my heart, he can't stay Davi."

"I know that," Mummy replied, her tone sombre. "But we owe it to him to get him one hundred per cent right. A caged environment at the Rescue for Oliver would simply just set him back. I'm not doing it, not after all he's endured."

"Well at least we'll have the dining room free for Christmas," Daddy acknowledged.

"Um..."

"What now?"

"I...um...well, I have an emergency coming home once the room has been sanitised.

"I don't believe you Davina. When?"

"This weekend."

"Well you can be the one to explain to Chanel and Cerys that here goes another year they have to eat their Christmas dinner on their knees when there's a lovely dining table there disused!" Daddy objected and threw the tea towel in the air before marching off.

"Oh crap! The girls won't be impressed. They won't be impressed at all!" Zena exclaimed.

And so, Oliver that very week relocated to the study and as much as the remainder of the brood had faith that he would not become a permanent resident of the Hanes brood, I still reserved judgement...and the impending niggle became more profound in time. This just wasn't Mummy's style at all!

Mama Lucy, the new pregnant mummy did take residence in the Hanes Maternity Pad, now freshly sanitised and prepared for new life.

Mummy ensured the floors were scrubbed clean and free of any potential infection.

Oliver's study door remained closed...but not for long!

The lock attached to the door was soon disregarded as Oliver finally showed an interest beyond his immediate surroundings.

"Just leave the door open," Daddy urged one Sunday morning much to my dismay. "He's not hurt anyone yet. He needs to learn how to integrate."

Feline inquisitiveness got the better of Thor and Holly and they brazenly entered 'his' room.

From the confines of his blue bed, he muttered horrid obscenities.

I crept in cautiously.

"What exactly happened to you to make you like this?" I whispered.

He raised his head sharply; I could almost feel his intense glare.

"Nowt to do with you, not anyone."

Finally! A response.

"We've all been through hardship you know," Thor offered encouragingly.

Simba sat beside me in the doorway wearily and with disinclination addressed Oliver, "Yeah, you're not on your own!"

My word! Simba had a heart!

"You've no idea, have you? I don't like you, none of you, so just keep your distance, all of you, got it? Especially YOU!" Oliver's vehemence was directed at Simba.

"You get too close and you'll regret it." He almost spat the warning.

With that, we retreated humbly.

He was never going to accept us I realised, somewhat dejectedly. It would take nothing short of a miracle to crack his tough exterior and mend his broken heart.

Jingles and Jangles

Within time, Oliver's hatred of us soon dissipated to that of dislike.

"It's completely understandable. He's probably had to fight for every single thing in his life. Being cared for and loved must indeed be a shock to his system," Grandpa Jasper advised.

It was a Saturday evening when street cat decided he wanted to explore; with a dubious step, he slinked through the door which was ajar; watching and listening.

And then a miracle happened.

Grandpa Jasper who had not climbed the stairs for a period of six years, slowly but surely mounted them. He puffed an exasperated sigh when he reached the top and slumped his hefty frame beside Oliver in exhaustion.

He took a moment to regain some composure, then breathlessly spoke to street cat.

"Everything will be alright young man. I'll stay up here for a while to keep you company."

"I don't want your company!" Oliver snarled.

"Listen here...I've not climbed these damn stairs for nothing!" Grandpa Jasper snapped uncharacteristically.

Exhaustion had evidently got the better of him.

"You need a friend more than you realise. If you want to fit in around here, I suggest you lose that 'street-cat' attitude of yours young man!" Grandpa Jasper reprimanded.

At that moment Simba flew up the stairs disbelievingly, "Bloody hell, fatty's actually managed the stairs!"

His mocking comment was heard yet ignored.

"Okay, I'll give it a go," Oliver's submission was tinged with reluctance.

"Happy now? I'll give it a go but just keep HIM away from me," He glared into Simba's eyes.

The days following led to events that were unprecedented. Grandpa Jasper deserted his longstanding fluffy bed in the lounge and took residence outside Oliver's study.

"Never in my life, I thought I'd see the day where he would climb the stairs again," Daddy was astounded.

"It must be because of Oliver," Mummy said, stroking the gentle giant whilst Oliver sat nearby. "Well, mister, we had better bring your bed upstairs."

She turned her attention to Oliver and stroked him with the same amount of fondness, "And as for you...well done little fella. You must have some special appeal going on here."

Jasper continued to lounge outside the study for the weeks that followed; mounting and dismounting the stairs with more confidence and agility.

"This exercise will be doing him the world of good. I've never seen him as active," Mummy said, watching him proudly. "And Oliver seems within his comfort zone with him, I think we've had ourselves a little breakthrough."

Indeed, it was. Oliver certainly became more inquisitive and almost daily would potter downstairs, dodging the others with his now solid, muscular lithe frame.

Christmas was approaching and the brood was becoming increasingly excited. "You'll love it Jack!" Tiddles exclaimed, "We have an enormous tree which we can trash and wrapping paper we can tear whilst Mummy tries to wrap presents. We get loads of treats, delicious turkey and gifts of our own."

It sounded amazing, almost magical.

Cerys arrived home shortly before Christmas, the girls too were evidently excited. Cerys fussed over a receptive Oliver as he pottered downstairs to greet her.

"Why's he still here mum?" her tone was sceptical.

"He's spending Christmas with us Cerys. He deserves that, at the very least. I have put an appeal out for him," Mummy said sincerely. "We just need him fattened up some more."
"You're not keeping him!" Cerys was aghast.
Mummy's reply was reassuring to us all. Good, she had no intention of keeping that street cat.

Mummy arrived home from work a tad subdued one day.
"What's up mum?" Cerys did that thing that humans do sometimes to reassure one another, a hug I think they call it.
"It's Sylvia."
"Sylvia from the Rescue?"
"Yes, she was diagnosed with terminal cancer earlier this year. She's deteriorated significantly. She's suffered a stroke and has gone into a hospice," Mummy said ruefully. "It's just so very unfair Cerys. I'll go up and visit her if she feels up to it."

I gasped, somewhat mortified by the news over our special Sylvia. All our prayers seemed futile at this moment in time.
Sylvia with her infectious smile and enormous heart was so undeserving of this inflicted illness.
"Do you think she'll get better?" I asked Holly remorsefully.
"I don't know Jack, I really don't know. All we can do is carry on hoping and praying."
And we did every day.

Oliver was gaining confidence by the day with Mummy previously luring him into a false sense of security; he now understood that if he wanted chicken, he had to work for it and take his place next to the microwave.
Magic, Holly, Thor and indeed Bambi surprisingly posed no threat to him and he would sit contentedly within close proximity.

I almost smiled to myself, Sylvia loved Oliver and had been following his journey. If only she could see him now...She would be thrilled to know of his recovery.

My relationship with Oliver? I unfortunately seemed to fall victim as his prey on more than one occasion. The others had long since mastered the art of swiftly dodging him with their graceful agility and precision. Me? I'd stumble right into the 'lion's den'; I'd either crash right into him as he sat boldly in the middle of the lounge or his swift swipe and snarl would indicate that I'd invaded his personal space.

"Mind where you're going!" he once almost spat the words at me.

I recoiled from the sting of his swipe and the venom in his voice.

"Lay off him!" Magic shielded me with his large frame as he confronted the foul-mouthed street cat. "Have a bit of respect. He can't see where he's going. Got it?"

"He has one eye, needs to learn how to use it," Oliver hissed.

"He can't see through that one either. So back off!"

I pawed the stinging spot on my nose repetitively where his claw had made contact.

"Oh sorry," Oliver mumbled to me, his tone surprisingly humble for a change. "Sorry mate."

He appeared to be a tad more understanding following Magic's opposition, however circumvention still continued to be a strenuous task for me where Oliver was concerned. The brood, despite their indifference to Oliver, certainly 'watched my back' and frequently warned me of potential collision and attack from him.

"Two steps to your left Jack."

"Take a swift one to the right."

"Turn, take a few steps back Jack."

"Jack, whoa, stop right there!"

"Steady on Jack, you're heading right for him."

Things were improving though and despite him being a complex character, we had begun to accept him and indeed his needs.

He enjoyed his own company and his own space. He loved human cuddles and spent hours on Mummy's knee whilst she sat in the study and it was in that very space he gained the privilege of owning a toy, probably for the first time in his life.

"He doesn't know what to do with it," Holly frowned.

"Well, go and help the poor boy," Grandpa Jasper instructed.

Holly, Peanut and Thor attempted to play with him on many an occasion and he would reciprocate, loving in particular the fluffy dangly toys. He would play with them for some time, loving a particular toy, then thunderstruck, he would pause, reality crashing down on him that he was letting his guard down with the others. He would then hiss and bat his opponent before retreating back into his blue bed.

As the Christmas season approached, the household became a hive of activity and music bellowed from the radio, as did festive smells which permeated the air.

Christmas, I realised was a time where there were many added obstacles in the home, many of which I welcomed.

"Oh Jack! Stop it," Mummy would groan in frustration as I skidded playfully across the blanket of wrapping paper on the floor. She sat there for hours, attempting to wrap boxes, bags and packages whilst I would coil myself in the sheets, chewing, clawing, tearing and biting, simply loving the textures and sounds.

My Auntie Jill made me the most incredible advent calendar and every day a little paper bag unravelled the most amazing gifts, which I shared with the brood.

Mummy arrived home from the Rescue one Saturday laden with sacks and boxes.

I sniffed curiously, knowing the familiar scent.

"No, no, no little man." Mummy removed the tantalising packages away from me. "These have to go to Santa for you, Jack."
With that, Daddy moved them away safely.

"Where's the big tree? They've not put it up yet!" exclaimed Candy. "Jack it's so much fun to play in!"
I awaited the arrival of this tree with excitement, my equilibrium however was somewhat thwarted by Cerys's outburst;
"What the bloody hell is THAT! You have got to be kidding?" she scolded as Mummy erected a contemporary and pathetic twig looking thing. "Where's our tree gone?"
"It's Jack's first Christmas and it's not safe for him. It's not worth the risk," Mummy answered whilst she tampered with the branches.
"I don't believe this! It's bad enough we have no garlands up anymore and the fact that we have to eat our Christmas dinner on our knee! But THIS..." she pointed to the twig in question in disgust, "...IT'S PATHETIC!"
"I agree," Candy echoed in distain. "Well said Cerys. There goes our fun in the tree, Jack."
"I've bought little decorations. See...." Mummy defended dangling a wooden object. Her words fell on deaf ears though as Cerys stormed out of the room shaking her head with Simba in tow.

Christmas morning finally arrived and true to Mummy and Daddy's word, Santa had been. The lounge floor was buried beneath a blanket of presents; some large, others small.
Cerys awoke early, something of a rarity.
"I wish Chanel was here," she said pensively.
It was Chanel's first Christmas away from home as she was working a shift in Newcastle.

"She'll be home tomorrow," Daddy reassured.

"I know, it's just not the same without her. Every cloud has a silver lining though, at least I'll get two Christmas dinners," Peanut licked his lips dreamily. "Yummy...All that turkey!"

"And cream off the trifle," Magic reminisced. "Mummy makes the most amazing trifle every year."

"She doesn't cook," I said confused. I'd been around long enough to establish Daddy did the majority of the cooking.

"She CAN'T cook, more to the point," Magic said, "Well, homemade lasagne and trifle is about her limit. I remember the year she had guests over and she caught me licking the fresh cream topping off her gigantic trifle. Boy, she was cross with me!"

"All that waste," from Peanut.

"No, not at all. She levelled it out, picked out the cat hairs and still fed it them," he chuckled.

Cerys's voice stilled our conversation,

"What time will you finish at the Rescue?"

"We shouldn't be long," Mummy said whilst extracting a copious amount of chicken from the fridge.

"Is that our breakfast, do you think?" I asked hopefully.

"No, it's for the resident cats," Peanut said, circling Mummy's ankles pleadingly. "We'll get ours later."

I soon discovered the Christmas day ritual involved Mummy and Daddy dedicating their Christmas morning caring for the cats and kittens at the Rescue. Alongside volunteers Chris and Patsy, they ensured all the furries were tended to before feeding them a scrumptious Christmas dinner.

Chanel and Cerys would usually prepare the vegetables for the Hanes household Christmas dinner and wait patiently for the parents to arrive home before opening their presents.

In that respect, this year was a little different; Mummy and Daddy met with their friends Lucy and Dave after the Rescue for a 'cheeky tipple' whilst Cerys enjoyed a Christmas dinner at Grandma Jenny and Grandad Pete's.

Needless to say, it was worth the wait, later on during the day we finally opened our presents. I never imagined Christmas to be so much fun and magical!

It was indeed a time to reflect upon how blessed I was and pray and think about all the homeless and abandoned souls out there, suffering and starving in somewhat harsh weather conditions. I too could have been one of them.

It was a time also to reflect on those who were suffering illness, such as Sylvia. I still couldn't quite get her out of my mind, her gentle disposition and her loving nature, a stark and cruel reminder of how unfair life could be at times.

"Come on then, time to see what Santa's brought you all," Daddy encouraged.

Eagerly we tore at the gift-wrap, sacks and boxes, anticipating what would be unravelled. Mummy and Daddy had certainly made dreams come true; we were showered with toys, cat trees and goodies. Auntie Jill likewise had bought us an amazing cat tree and sacks full of sensory toys and delectable edible treats.

"WOW!" an enchanted Simba exclaimed as he dangled from one of the new cat trees. "Never before have we had a Christmas quite like this!"

"Um Mum...," Cerys grumbled, rummaging through the debris of gift-wrap, "This just puts things into perspective. How is it that they've got all THIS and I've um...only got three presents?"

"Christmas is for the children," Daddy laughed, throwing me one of my new sparkly balls. "You won't be disappointed when you open them."

We spent the remainder of the day climbing, chasing, clawing and playing.

"Let's not forget little Oliver, eh..."

Mummy extracted a cat tree and some toys before heading in the direction of upstairs.

"I wish he'd come down stairs more and join in," Magic grumbled.

"He's happy up there," Grandpa Jasper reassured. "Trust me. Like humans, some cats just enjoy their own space. Look at Treacle, she's very much the same. He's causing no harm to anyone."

And that was the true reality of the situation; he certainly wasn't. On the contrary, what was increasingly worrying was that he was blending more and more into a brood that had inadvertently accepted him.

Dark and sombre beginnings

With Christmas and New Year celebrations behind us, the house had regained some element of normality. The home was stripped bare of chaos, noise and Christmas decorations. Chanel had returned to Newcastle, Cerys likewise to Liverpool, whilst Mummy and Daddy resumed their mundane working patterns.

We, of course, had plenty to occupy us with our new toys and magnificent cat trees.

Mummy arrived home from work one day and instead of food being the focal point, it was the dreaded cat carrier.

"C'mon little man," she said as she eased me into the carrier. "Mummy's taking you somewhere special."

The drive was short and once we reached our destination, I lay there curiously as Mummy walked through some doors in at a reception area.

As she proceeded to walk through the hallways, my presence sparked some level of fuss and attention and several times Mummy had to wait whilst I was cooed over.

Finally, Mummy stopped once she reached the corner of a large room, a bedside area.

She placed my carrier gently on the floor whilst she leaned over to greet the person in the bed.

"Hey Sylvia," she said softly, "I've brought someone special to see you today."

Sylvia! She'd actually brought me to see Sylvia!

"You can't get to the Rescue so I've brought the Rescue to see you."

"You have?" Sylvia's usual bright and cheery voice was quieter, much quieter than normal; still softly spoken though.

Mummy lifted me from my carrier and leaned forward towards Sylvia.

Her peripheral vision enabled her to identify who I was.

"Aaaaw Jack, sweetheart," she mumbled, "you've brought Jack."

I wriggled in Mummy's arms, eager to get closer to Sylvia. Placed on the bed I gently edged towards her right side, which was less affected from her stroke. I rested my head beside her and placed my paw on her hand.

"Hello sweetheart," Sylvia whispered, "fancy coming to see your Auntie Sylvia, eh? How's our Holly and Oliver?"

Slowly Mummy released her grasp and she removed her hands from my back. I nestled forward into Sylvia whilst Mummy continued to speak. Her husband Rod sat to the right of the bed, his eyes brimming with tears at the sight that lay before him.

Sensing Sylvia's pain, illness, her needs...I simply lay there passively for some length of time, my paw in her outstretched hand, comforting her, not wanting to move. At that moment in time nothing else mattered, everything else blurred into insignificance.

It was just me and Sylvia.

Sometime later a nurse stopped beside the foot of the bed.

"Aaaaw just look, he's beautiful. Cats certainly know, don't they? He knows. Our resident cat Arnie has barely left her side. Every day he's been to visit. Hasn't he Sylvia?"

"He has." Sylvia whispered weakly.

"Arnie's even got one of your knitted blankets, hasn't he Sylvia?" from Rod.

"Yes." She sighed, her acute tiredness evident.

At that very moment in time, I wished and prayed more than ever for Sylvia to regain her health and vibrant energy; wished for the horrid cancer to go away. I wished to see her again at the Rescue; the beautiful, gentle soul that she was, offering cuddles, love and affection.

A silent tear trickled from my one eye. Why God? I asked. Why?

Those precious moments Sylvia and I shared there on the bed that day were something beyond comprehension; a moment in time that was priceless as I lay there, my paw in her hand, as she gained such profound comfort from my presence.

Sadly, I never saw my Auntie Sylvia ever again.

With deep regret Sylvia passed away several days later after losing a heroic battle against cancer. Mummy and some of the volunteers were blessed enough to spend some precious final moments with Sylvia during her final hours.
God had certainly gained an Angel.
"She'll be all around us in spirit Little Jack. You must believe that," Mummy murmured after breaking the devastating news to us, her own anguish was palpable. "And she'll never be forgotten at the Rescue for who she was and all that she did. She loved that kitten room dearly so we'll be renaming it 'Sylvia's Sanctuary". We'll hold a special event that will be a celebration of her life and her ashes will be planted in a special rose bush in memory of her, the remarkable woman she was." Mummy turned her attention to Daddy, her eyes brimming with tears, "Arnie the resident cat hardly ever left Sylvia's side you know. He was with her till the very end."

The days, weeks even, that followed were tinged with sadness as Mummy and Daddy came to terms with the loss of a friend. Sylvia was an incredible lady, one who would be dearly missed. Understandably, there were many to consider, Sylvia's grieving husband Rod; the volunteers who were so very close to Sylvia and of course supporters of the Rescue who had become so fond of her over the years.
During the bleak month of January, Countess Tiddula Tiddles was booked in for a dental at Crown House Vets and Baby Bambi similarly was booked in for her neuter process.

Tiddles, well, despite her wondrous fangs, had dental issues, which needed tending to.

"Nothing to worry about little ones," Mummy consoled Tiddles and Bambi during the morning of the procedures. We all followed Mummy frantically awaiting our breakfast with rumbling tummies.

You see, nil by mouth for one in the Hanes household meant nil by mouth for all, just until the cats in question were transported to the vets. The remainder of the brood would then enjoy a late hearty breakfast. The delay in feeding time did however lead to much agitation, especially from the likes of Oliver who was by now used to having his chicken upon demand.

"They better bloody well leave my fangs be!" Tiddles gasped in profound horror.

"Don't you worry Tiddles, no ones going to touch them fangs of yours, I promise you that...and Bambi, you'll be just fine. Just think Tiddles, they only took one of my eyes out, not both. They're not that bad," I reassured.

"You'll both be fine," Zena confirmed, "it'll be over before you know it. And Bambi, you need this doing to stop you having babies."

We all bid them good luck before they left, knowing they would return safely.

"As long as her fangs are safe," Mummy had joked to Clare the vet the day previous.

Tiddles' fangs were her trademark after all and she certainly prided herself on those precious pincers of hers.

Lunchtime arrived and as usual Mummy returned home to tend to Lucy's babies who were almost available for adoption and of course to spend some quality time with ourselves.

Her phone suddenly rang as she was in this process of replenishing food for the babies.

"Davina just to clarify both Tiddles and Bambi are fine following their surgery," the voice spoke through the handset. "But...um...well Tiddles, um, you see her teeth were in a far worse condition than expected. We dreaded which vet was the one who'd have to break the news to you but I'm sorry she's had to lose the fangs."
Silence.

"You're kidding right?" Mummy exclaimed. "Not her fangs!"
"Davina they were rotten, they needed extracting. I'm so sorry. I dreaded this call. They had to go, Davina, they were decaying and obviously causing her discomfort. As were the other teeth."
A further silence whilst Mummy absorbed the information.
"Thank you, Clare," she finally managed, "really, thank you. The main thing is that she's okay, that's all that matters. If they were causing her pain then they needed taking out. I agree."

"Oh my! Tiddles is gonna be one pissed puddy tat!" Oliver exclaimed from the kitchen.
"Language, Oliver!" from Grandpa Jasper. "You're not on the streets now."
"She's gonna look like a right numpty!" Simba smirked. "And that ridiculous name will have to go."
"Whatever she looks like, you'll all treat her with respect when she returns home," Grandpa Jasper admonished. "Remember, we don't chastise anyone for their looks. I won't have it."
Oliver strutted through the lounge and took himself back upstairs, muttering as he went along, "A right bleedin' dysfunctional lot we have here. What, you with no eye; him with a bulbous tummy, now her with no teeth. Whatever next?"

And so, the brood eagerly awaited Tiddles' and Bambi's return later that evening.

"You'll have to tell me what she looks like," I said to Holly. "I do hope she's not too bothered. Mummy's right, at least she's okay, that's the main thing." It was times like this I really wished I had the luxury of sight.

Finally, they arrived home.

"Not a word. Not a bloody word! From any of you!" Tiddles hissed with a profound lisp as she marched through the lounge and into the kitchen. "I'll never trust that bloody woman again! She promised me, she did. *'Don't you worry Tiddles, no ones going to touch them fangs of yours, I promise you that'.* Lying sod!" she mimicked Mummy's previous words with prolific disdain.

"Where's the food? I WANT MY FOOD!"

She glared at Mummy resentfully, as the food was being dished out and her ranting continued,

"Then that bloody vet, to top it off, tells Mummy to feed me lightly. *'She'll be sore having all those teeth extracted. Feed her lightly'* she said. I DON'T THINK SO!"

Tiddles' fury was profound, her pride wounded. Her mood improved some when she was provided food; eagerly she devoured a bowl full of chicken, her sore mouth by no means affecting her ability to eat.

Bambi sauntered into the kitchen, a little more reserved than normal but holistically unaffected with her own procedure.

"Um...I AM here, you know. Don't worry about me, I'm fine." She said waspishly, a tad peeved that the focal point of attention was indeed Tiddles' fangs.

Sensing her hurt, I devoted the remainder of the evening comforting her.

"You look a right bugger..." Simba teased Tiddles a little later on.

"Well I think you look kinda cute," Thor offered, glaring forebodingly at Simba.

"I agree."

"You look more of a lady."

"The lisp is cute too."

"Much better looking."

"Very flattering."

The brood offered a catalogue of encouraging compliments to Tiddles.

"You think so?" she asked, absorbing the polite remarks provided.

"I'm sure you look pretty, still." I offered numbly, not quite knowing what to say.

"You look splendid, dear girl. I would certainly say Mummy's new name for you is very fetching indeed." smiled Grandpa Jasper.

And so, this was the day 'Countess Tiddula Tiddles' became 'Countess Tiddles the Fangless Wonder'!

The gloomy month took somewhat of a twist on January 8th. Mummy returned from the Rescue laden with parcels for me. These were from my Auntie Jill. I could scent out those parcels effortlessly. Weekly, my angel still continued to send me gifts to share amongst the brood and almost daily she would still enquire after me.

On this occasion Mummy came home with a scrap of paper also. Hesitantly, she presented it to Daddy. She always chose her moments well when she was up to mischief and Daddy having a Budweiser in his grasp was a sure indicator his mood would be mellow.

"What's this?" he asked.

"Confirmation."

"Of what?"

"Look and see," She encouraged.

Silently he unfolded the paper and read its contents.

"Oliver...You've adopted him." Not a shout, nor an exclamation. Just a whisper, the relief in his voice was evident.

"Darren, he's overcome such a milestone. Just look at him. He's never going to be quite like the others in terms of integrating but he's lovable, he's happy and more to the point, he's settled." She pointed towards the fearless street cat who was already awaiting his chicken fix, "He just belongs now." Mummy defended, fearful of Daddy's opposition.

However, there was none. Daddy simply walked over to Oliver and stroked him, "See buddy, everything's turned out alright for you."

Astounded, I marched into the lounge to Granpda Jasper, "I don't bloody believe it! He's staying! She's actually gone and adopted him."

"First Jack, mind that language of yours. And secondly, it was evidently going to happen. He's become part of the brood now. You, after all you've been through yourself, can't deny the boy a little security and happiness."

"But she promised!" I objected sulkily.

"Sometimes one's heart takes over Jack. Mummy and Daddy have invested a lot into Oliver, more than any of us could ever imagine. He's here and there's only one thing we can all do about it."

"There is?" I asked, hopeful.

"Yes. Accept it."

I wanted to say that Grandpa Jasper wasn't right on this occasion but after much reflection and looking at Oliver's journey and progress, I eventually submitted. Indeed, who was I to deprive any cat of a loving home? Me, of all furries?

The news astounded the brood; Simba in particular who fought desperately to maintain his status as 'top cat'.

Neither cat particularly liked one another, both had that dominant and competitive streak and both would stake each other out with glaring eyes, pupils dilated.

"Just stop it! The pair of you!" Magic scolded impatiently. "If you can't tolerate one another, then just keep your distance."

Eventually, within time, their dominant rivalry subsided some and they did indeed keep a healthy distance from one another. Oliver, I suspected was much of a ladies man; his only show of affection other than that towards humans was his very amorous approach with the girls at times. Bambi and Holly in particular were his favourites and on many an occasion he would dine with them, sharing the offerings from his bowl. I showed no malice or jealousy though, he posed no threat and after all, there was no denying that these two were my special girls. They always came back to me.

It was a week following the news, volunteer Samantha handed Mummy a package and a card. It was a gift from an unexpected source; our Sylvia.

Tearfully, Mummy read the card

Samantha explained to Mummy, "This was the last blanket Sylvia ever knitted before she was taken ill. She was kind of hoping you'd be keeping him. Before she died she asked me to make sure Oliver was to have this."

Mummy unfolded the blue crochet blanket, truly a special gift from Sylvia, "It's beautiful. Oliver will love this, Samantha."

Oliver certainly did, daily he would snooze in his blue bed with his blue crochet blanket. Frequently when his bedding required washing, a temporary bed would be provided; Oliver however objected. He wouldn't entertain any other bed whatsoever

other than his special blue one so in protest he would sulk moodily until his unique bed was readily available once more.
Certainly, a tale of rags to riches, the title street cat had now become more of a term of endearment...Oliver, once deprived and neglected now enjoyed the finer luxuries in life and received them upon demand.

No longer Orphan Oliver...Master Oliver Hanes was finally born!

January was bleak in more ways than one; the loss of Sylvia, Tiddles' teeth, a viral infection which affected the entire brood and then there was raising concern over Tiny Treacle, only one week following Tiddles' surgery.
Her behaviour was becoming more and more erratic, she even on numerous occasions ventured downstairs on the rampage for additional offerings of food, something of an extreme anomaly for a timid little soul like Treacle.
Despite her insatiable appetite she had suffered a rapid amount of weight loss within a short space of time.
"This just isn't right," professed Mummy, "the weight loss is a concern, her eating patterns and her behaviour's just bizarre."
"Book her in at the vets," Daddy frowned, "Jack's booked in tomorrow anyway, isn't he?"
I was indeed, it seemed that whenever we did contract a viral infection, the remainder of the brood were far more robust and could fight off infection effortlessly; myself, it always seemed to take a little while longer and with additional medication.

Feeling somewhat under the weather still, Treacle accompanied me to the vets the following day. It was Clare whom we saw; guarded. Treacle and I ensured she went nowhere near our teeth, fangs in particular. No, she'd had Tiddles already, she certainly wasn't getting her wicked way with us!

A further course of antibiotics it was for me and Treacle squirmed in distaste, as it was her turn to be examined.

"What we're probably looking at here is a typical case of over-active thyroid," Clare stated, examining her thoroughly. "The symptoms she's presenting, with the rapid weight loss, is a really strong indicator. We'll do her bloods and take it from there."

"Well if it is, what's the prognosis?" Mummy's voice was laced with concern.

"Cats can go on to live a reasonably healthy and normal life. There's a lot to consider here as thyroid levels can, for one, affect her kidneys and then there's her blood pressure. First thing's first, let's do the bloods and then take it from there."

"It can be treated though?"

"It can but I'm afraid it would mean her remaining on medication for life."

"Good grief!" Treacle hissed aghast. "I'd rather her remove my fangs. Nothing's straight forward with this vet!"

Treacle was whisked away to have her bloods taken and before too long we were on our way back home.

Apprehensively, Mummy awaited on the vet results and when her phone rang, Clare did indeed confirm Mummy's worst fear. "Treacle's thyroid levels are significantly high. She'll need to begin medication straight away and we'll need to see her again in four-weeks-time for more bloods and a blood pressure check so ideally, she'll need to remain at the vets for the day. We need her in a relatively calm state for her blood pressure. She's was a bit jittery and anxious when we did her bloods earlier so I'd recommend nil by mouth when she next comes in."

Clare continued to explain, "With this condition, it's important we monitor every few weeks and it may well be a case of altering medication and dosage to get her thyroid levels within range."

What followed for tiny Treacle within the following few weeks was a rigorous daily regime of medication.

"Not again!" she'd grimace as she saw Mummy or Daddy coming at her with her medication and would scramble under the bed in fear.

Mummy soon became wise to her antics however of holding her tablet under her tongue then later spitting it out. The monotonous regime became lengthier whilst she had to be held for longer periods of time.

"We're still out of range," Clare stated following her next visit. "We'll need to increase her thyroid medication and she'll also need additional medication for her blood pressure which is also not balanced."

"She hates the tablets," Mummy said desolately, "every day's a horrible ordeal for her."

"Then she can certainly go on the liquid Thyronorm. We'll get her there, don't you worry. We've caught this early enough to do something about it."

Treacle's behaviour continued to be inconsistent and her jittery nature took some adapting to, from us all. The timid little girl had evolved into a jumpy, irrational little soul who would seem to run and jump around aimlessly.

Monthly she would spend a day at the vets for her bloods to be taken and her blood pressure to be checked. Some months she would behave more erratically than others but with time her behaviour seemed to regulate some.

"We'll get you sorted out, little angel," Mummy said with determination after pinning her down to administer further medication, "we're making good progress so far."

It was with sadness we witnessed little Treacle braving her medication ritual every day. But mummy said she would improve and we could do nothing other than have faith in her words, Treacle in particular.

Despite the strain of worry beginning to take its toll on Mummy, her care for our brood and her dedication to the 'Hanes maternity Pad' remained unaffected.
Mama Lucy and her babies were all successfully rehomed and the room was refilled instantaneously with another emergency. From what I could ascertain from Mummy's conversations, Mama Dottie had gone into labour at the Rescue on the Saturday morning and had apparently become distressed, the first kitten became dislodged and was wedged for an unhealthy period of time.
I overheard Mummy telling Daddy later about the very dedicated supporter called Steve who had only called in the rescue that morning to donate food. This visit however, resulted with him transporting my Mummy and the distressed cat in question to the emergency vets. The rapid response and immediate veterinary treatment resulted in survival for both the mummy and babies; all kittens being delivered by emergency caesarean section.
This volunteer's experience at the rescue was certainly an unprecedented one!

January evolved into a dismal February and it was with concern one morning that Mummy spoke to Daddy,
"Jasper's not right."
That was mummy's terminology of stating there was a problem, we'd long since discovered this.
"What are you mithering over now?"
"His weight loss, well, it's far too sudden. I've found a lump also."
This conversation certainly highlighted just how much weight our Grandpa had lost over a short period of time.

Grandpa's abundant rolls of blubber were certainly something we'd become accustomed to, but upon reflection, he had undeniably shed a substantial amount of weight, his back bone could now be felt and as the rolls of fat gradually disappeared from around his chin, a slender neck line developed. The once surplus layers had disintegrated some, leaving him svelte in comparison to the likes of Countess Tiddles, who seemed to have developed a newfound gluttony since the extraction of her precious fangs...eating was evidently easier as she never appeared to stop!

So, a trip to the vets it was for dear old Grandpa.

"That's a substantial amount of weight loss there," Clare stated after comparing his previous weight to that of his now smaller frame, "there's got to be an explanation. Don't get me wrong; it's good that he's lost weight but not so rapidly. I recommend we take some bloods to see what's going on here."

"And the lump?"

The vet examined Grandpa thoroughly, "That's a cyst, nothing to be concerned over. We can drain that now."

So, once the procedure was completed along with blood tests, Mummy returned home with a somewhat disgruntled Jasper.

"We just have to await the outcome now, little fella," she frowned, her positivity plagued with worry.

"Bloody hate going to the vets!" Grandpa muttered once released from his carrier. Glumly, he tottered over to the comfort and normality of his bed.

"LANGUAGE GRANDPA!" I reprimanded, finally rejoicing in the opportunity to scold him for a change.

"I tell you. I can't win! I'm a fatty; always have been. *'Too fat he is!'* That's all I ever hear. Then once I do lose weight, I'm subject to THIS! Can't win with these damn humans sometimes."

"They're only worried," my humble attempt to pacify him fell upon deaf ears; he was clearly piqued.

Mummy was on tender-hooks for the few hours following, that was until she received the long-awaited call from the vets.

"Well, I'm surprised I must say. But it's good news," Clare's voice could be heard over the loud speaker.

"Has everything come back normal with his bloods?" Mummy asked with a sigh of relief.

"Absolutely normal. It seems it may well be the additional exercise which has resulted in his recent weight loss."

So, it appeared we did actually have something to thank Master Oliver Hanes for. Jasper's preference to be near him, accompanied by additional exercise with a daily workout on the stairs, had resulted in him shedding a superfluous 2kg.

Jasper was relieved that there was nothing sinister underlying with his results and this news somewhat caused his bad mood to dissipate.

Mummy patted him on the head with pride, her relief evident, "Well then Grandpa, you should be proud of yourself," she smiled.

He purred his response.

"You're still a fat ass, I can't see what all the fuss is about," Simba scoffed.

"Well, Oliver's clearly done him more good than you!" Magic condemned, then diverted his attention to Jasper. "Well done old chap! Keep up the good work...just make sure you go easy on those Dreamies now."

So, it was with very great exultation and pride that Grandpa Jasper continued to trot around the home, fostering a more muscular approach, not quite 'climbing' material with his still hefty frame, but he moved with more confidence and agility than ever before.

Week upon week, Oliver continued to develop a new-found confidence which had obviously been aided some by Grandpa's resilience and determination. It was ironic how the two had benefited one another, on completely different levels of course.

He would prowl in different rooms portentously throughout the day, disconcerted by some of us only when we invaded his personal space. Grandpa, Magic, Thor and certainly Bambi and Holly were able to brush right past him and he would remain unperturbed. This was a privilege that many of us remained indifferent to.

The remainder of our furry family, including myself, certainly had to keep a distance, otherwise without doubt, would suffer the wrath of Oliver.

His vulgarities, spits and hisses however, no longer unearthed fear in us; we had grown to accept his anti-social characteristics and indeed accept Oliver for himself.

"Do you think he's happy here?" I asked Thor, somewhat concerned, "living as a recluse can't be much fun, can it?"

"I wouldn't worry yourself over it Jack. You don't eat copious amounts, develop a healthy coat, purr on your hooman's knee nor explore the home in the company of others if you're not happy. The lad's fine, he just enjoys his own space, a bit like Treacle I guess."

"But Treacle plays," I objected.

"Remember where he's come from, well, he's probably never been taught how to play, nor ever been shown what a toy is, for that matter."

"He plays with toys though, I've heard him."

"Yes, he's probably stumbled across this pleasure by himself but he's not been blessed with the opportunity of socialising with others in his past to know how rewarding integration can be."

There was indeed many a time where Oliver would frenetically play with toys and douse himself in catnip. Likewise, he would climb and dangle from his own cat tree in the study. So yes, I surmised, maybe he was happy here.

Poor Treacle was another story; she still had to endure a rigorous medication regime every day accompanied by her monthly visits at the vets. Her thyroid levels were improving, but as the vet explained, there was much to be considered and the dosage of medication given was dependant on her thyroid levels and indeed her blood pressure.

"Bloody well hate spending the day at the vets!" she grimaced after one of her daily visits.

"So do we!" Simba retorted. "Our breakfast is always put on the back burner with your 'nil-by-mouth' business. Preposterous!"

"Do they hurt you?" I asked, concerned.

"No, no! Not at all! They're so good with me but the truth is, well, all this medication and the blood tests are beginning to take its toll. Every time Mummy or Daddy approach me for a cuddle, I recoil. I just see them coming at me with the meds all the time."

My heart went out to her, a quiet little soul she was, so loving of her parents and the ordeal she had endured was evidently affecting her on an emotional level.

"You'll have to go through this for life?" I frowned.

"Not necessarily," Treacle perked some. "Clare the vet has suggested the option of radiation or corrective surgery to help eradicate a lifetime of dependency on drugs. The problem is my thyroid levels need to be within range to perform this surgery. It's hard going, at the moment, but I do have faith they'll get me there."

I grimaced, sensing her distress, "Which option do you think Mummy will go for?"

"Maybe the operation," Treacle replied. "Mummy says at only seven years old, I have a whole life ahead of me. As much as I detest the medication and close monitoring at present, our parents only want the best for me. I've come to accept, things have been put in place for my benefit."

I could only hope and pray for Treacle. I'd witnessed her decline over the past few months, she appeared well health-wise but lacked the lustre and love for life she once had; the daily medication regime had certainly changed her, married with her erratically behaved condition.
They'll get her there, I thought with confidence, after all, they'd got me to that amazing point of no return, amongst many more little ones.

When Mummy arrived home unexpectedly with yet another pregnant cat, it took me by no surprise, after all, the 'Hanes Maternity Pad' was seldom empty.
Luna, she was called, a silver and white semi longhaired beauty by all accounts, who had sadly been left behind when her previous owner vacated the premises.
I grimaced as Mummy carried her upstairs to her room; not because of her presence, no, simply because of the calculated callousness and malice from some humans.
"I don't believe it!" Simba exclaimed, peering into the carrier. "She's got extra bloody toes!"
Grandpa Jasper intervened, "Polydactyl is the word and..."
"We know... 'MIND YOUR LAUNGAUGE!'" we mimicked simultaneously.

Needless to say, Mummy spent many hours shut away in that room, nurturing the very subdued girl; calming her and becoming acquainted with each other.

19th March was a Sunday morning, my usual frenetic playtime slot was disturbed by the sound of Mummy's phone; it was volunteer Chris from the Rescue.

"Lavender's gone into labour," he informed, "she's struggled a bit with the first, didn't quite know what to do."

"I'm on my way Chris."

"We'll carry on once I get back, little man, eh!" She turned her attention to me, stroking me. I chirped my reply.

My playtime was postponed as Mummy, halted in her tracks, took off for the Rescue with Daddy in tow.

Mummy had explained to us that Lavender, likewise to Luna, was also an abandoned cat, their previous owners had simply left them as a stray to fend for themselves. She had accepted her into the Rescue the day previous from the new tenants who had been feeding her. Mummy informed them Lavender was close to birth as her teats were already full of milk.

Taking this into account, I did understand my sudden abandonment, after all, this issue was far more prevailing at present. I knew my playtime would resume soon upon her return.

How wrong could one be?

The parents returned home early afternoon, somewhat pacified that Lavender had delivered her five babies; all appearing to be in good health.

Upon entering the house, Mummy was startled to discover Simba, Max and Peanut running amok. That was the moment Mummy knew!

"Oh, crickey! It's Luna, I think she's had the babies!" cried Mummy.

Despite such confinement of the foster mummies, our brood could certainly detect when labour or new birth had taken place; hormones flying around in abundance.

"Oh no! I dread to think where she's had them! I left her out of the crate this morning!" Mummy exclaimed, rushing up the stairs.

She shut herself away in the room and from beyond the door we listened inquisitively to the squeals of new-borns.

"Everything okay?" Daddy called.

Mummy exited the room with an exasperated sigh, "Yeah, she's fine and all four babies are good. She's only decided to have them in the cat tree, little monkey. They're all safely tucked away in their bed now."

"All babies are well?"

"They are...aaaw and three of the four have extra tootsies too."

"Good grief! Now she's cooing over extra toes! C'mon, let's resume this playtime Jack. We've wasted enough time already!" Max grunted officiously.

And so, the Maternity Pad was once again back in action, thus accepted by all.

Little Jack Lion Heart

Within my short life, already, I seemed to have endured my fair share of illnesses; first my blindness which in all honesty I'd never fallen victim to. The darkness had simply become a way of life for me and I'd learned to accept the obliteration of colour. It was other numerous relapses that put my health at risk. The initial relapse occurred only several weeks after my arrival at the Hanes residence and my sudden lethargy and dehydration was an indicator to Mummy and Daddy that I was indeed poorly. The severity of this episode required emergency intervention at Armac Vets where they had me on a drip overnight. Sick and confused, I helplessly slumped in my cage in the isolation unit fearing Mummy and Daddy had abandoned me. At this time, poignant thoughts still haunted me from my harrowing and precarious time on the streets. Being isolated and alone once again, only caused me to question my future.

The Lion Heart fighter I was, I overcame this and indeed many subsequent bouts of illness such as viral infections, pancreatitis, flu like symptoms and even episodes of conjunctivitis. Such episodes were not as much of a challenge to the others, however, with my low immune system; the slightest ailment seemed to affect me on a gargantuan level.

My worse bout of illness by far occurred so spontaneously, so unexpected and so very, very serious.

It was a normal Monday morning on the 21st March; or so Mummy thought...

Mundanely at 5.00am prompt, my Mummy and Daddy awoke with the alarm clock bellowing out music. The house routinely came alive with the usual orchestrated chaos of the humans preparing for work, alongside the clattering of dishes and the banging whilst litter trays were being sanitised.

Uncomfortable some, I didn't quite feel myself. No, to be honest, poorly was actually how I felt. I shuffled around on the bedroom floor, washing myself repeatedly with vigour. Desperately, all I wanted was a wee-wee but nothing was happening. I helplessly washed myself in hope that I could resolve the issue but to no avail.

I jumped onto the bed next to Mummy, wriggling in acute discomfort.

"Darren!" Mummy bellowed loudly.

From downstairs Daddy replied.

"I don't think Jack's right!" she shouted, her tone concerned.

Daddy's footsteps clambered up the stairs and he stroked my head comfortingly.

"He's fine, there's nothing wrong with him. You worry too much over nothing," he dismissed.

"Please! Please! Listen to Mummy...I really don't feel fine..." I meowed up at him despairingly.

It was times like this when I desperately wished humans could fully communicate with us cats and vice versa. Sadly, this wasn't the case to be.

"I'm telling you..." Mummy insisted, "...he's not right! He's been cleaning himself for far too long. He looks uncomfortable. Don't you poppet?" Mummy turned her attention to me with reassuring strokes.

"That's what cats do," Daddy explicated whilst impatiently jingling his work keys. "He's been fine in himself. Haven't you lad?" He paused momentarily, looking at me. "Um, well, I suppose now you mention it, I saw him doing that last night too. Get him booked in," Daddy's tone had changed some to that of anxiety.

"I'm not taking any chances, I'll make him an appointment after work," Mummy replied. "Something's amiss here."

My Mummy, my saving grace; I looked up at her in relief and with such gratitude. She knew me so intently, knew all of my habits and characteristics and could always discern when something wasn't quite right. Always. Thankfully her astuteness when noticing I wasn't well, enabled me to receive the appropriate veterinary attention in good time.

"Thank you Mummy," I whispered in a soft purr. "Thank you."

After cuddles and strokes, both Mummy and Daddy left for work, leaving me to ponder what the outcome of this particular veterinary visit would be.

Apprehensive and in discomfort, this particular day seemed like an eternity, waiting for Mummy to arrive home from work.

Mummy finally arrived, accompanied with her usual white cat carrier.

Pepper's sudden roar propelled me into alert mode.

"Crap! She's here with 'the' carrier! Run! You KNOW the drill...Magic take a left; Thor you to the right; the rest of you take your positions. Take position NOW!"

The scurry of rushed claws along the flooring pricked my ears even further...the cat carrier most often meant one thing to us all, and one thing only; A TRIP TO THE VETS!

On this occasion, I felt too poorly to take my position.

Within moments Mummy gently eased me into the carrier.

Unusually frazzled; I panted, scratched, cried and clawed on my journey to the vets. I knew deep down I had serious problems.

I listened on attentively and worriedly as Mummy explained my symptoms to the vet, Jonathan. Yet another thorough examination! He prodded, poked and inserted that thing for my temperature, no stone unturned with him. The room went silent, so very silent. I could sense mummy's anxiety building.

"He has a blockage, "Jonathan explained, his tone quite sinister. "This is serious Davina, until we operate we don't know quite what we're dealing with; a tumour, kidney failure or crystals. If his kidneys have been affected already, the anaesthetic alone could be dangerous. He needs operating on….now!"

In a surreal state of shock, with shaky hands Mummy signed the consent form, her eyes brimming with tears. I could sense her profound fear.

Within the confines of my carrier, I feared the worst as I know Mummy did. I cowered in fear whilst Jonathan carried me away.

The end for Little Jack?

Disorientated still from the effects of the anaesthetic I scrambled frenetically in my carrier, unsure of where I was or indeed what was happening.

The vet Jonathan's voice gave some clarification to where I was and indeed that I'd pulled through from my operation.

I could tell Mummy and Daddy were within close proximity, given the poignant whiff of Mummy's perfume attacking my nostrils.

"So, we've successfully cleared the blockage by catheterising him," Jonathan explained to Mummy and Daddy. "Good news, there's no tumour and his kidney function appears to be normal. What I HAVE found are struvite crystals, these are crystal-like formations that are relatively small in size and are primarily made up of magnesium, ammonium and phosphate. It's these crystals that have caused the blockage. It's good you brought Jack in with early detection, knowing there was something amiss here. This kind of blockage can propel them into kidney failure quite rapidly."

A brief silence whilst Mummy and Daddy absorbed what the vet was telling them.

"Will it happen again?" asked Daddy apprehensively.

"It's a possibility, yes. I've taken bloods to establish whether there's anything else going on and he will be going home on two lots of medication. It's imperative you monitor his urine output, especially over the next few days."

"So, I'll need to isolate him from the others?" more of a rhetorical question from Mummy.

"Definitely...for now. It's crucial to treat this early and if you see any recurrence or warning symptoms again, you bring Jack straight down here."

The directness of the vets' tone made me shudder; made me aware of the severity of my condition.

"He'll be quite sore at the moment too, so bear that in mind."

"You're not kidding mister!" I grimaced and fretfully squirmed within the perimeter of my carrier. "First you remove my eye, then my bloody crown jewels here...and now THIS!"

My voice went unheard of course.

"How do we prevent this happening again?" Mummy asked hastily.

"Well...Jack will need a special diet from now on. A special urinary feline diet would reduce the saturation of urine. When struvite is a problem, these diets are a necessity in terms of making the urine more dilute and more acidic."

"Can he have other food also, you know, like his tuna loins and Dreamies?" asked Daddy.

"No. Absolutely nothing," Jonathan the vet replied.

I pouted... this vet, I was seriously beginning to dislike him more and more. First my winky is sore, now he's telling them I can't have my normal food; Dreamies; tuna loins, my Good as it Looks. I disliked him more than ever!

In my drugged state, the journey home was tedious. I wriggled, slithered and slumped, trying to combat the lethargy.

"Crap! What the hell is going on here?" Simba exclaimed as Mummy and Daddy carried me through to the kitchen.

"Hey Jack, you ok?"

"What's happened Jack?"

"Hey little fella, where've you been?"

An echo of purrs trailed behind me as I was transported safely into the kitchen.

Once gently lifted from my cage I began to scramble and fall helplessly everywhere, I remember wanting to be near Mummy and Daddy as they sat on the floor next to me reassuringly.

In a cloud of disorientation, I wobbled and fell, unable to gain my balance.

"Dear Lord...What's wrong with the little chap?" Even Grandpa Jasper roused from his deep habitual lazy sleep, trotting towards the kitchen. "He looks like Mummy and Daddy on a typical Saturday night!"

Magic steered forward to sniff me, "He's been to the vets. I can smell it on him. Gather the others...He needs us right now. Go!" and with that, soon after, despite my sluggish state, I was comforted by forthcoming affection.

I was hungry, so hungry but the food Mummy and Daddy offered me was somewhat putrid. I scraped my paws along the floor and turned my nose up.

"He doesn't like this stuff," Daddy complained.

"He'll have to adjust," Mummy replied sternly, "they all will, and it's for his own good. No more treats, no more normal food. This diet's important for him and we're sticking with it. If it means preventing this happening again, then 'needs must' I suppose."

"Well what about the others?" Daddy exclaimed, "How the heck do you expect to separate them at meal times?"

"We'll do it. We'll cope ...we have to," Mummy pondered some. "No more grazing for them."

I was also beginning to dislike Mummy more and more at this moment in time.

"We need to do this Darren. They saved him tonight. Things aren't brilliant and it'll take some adjusting but we'll get there."

But I don't want to adjust, I pleaded silently.

Staggering around the kitchen, I tried to gather my bearings. So, things were about to change some for me...and not for the better it seemed. No more delicious treats and for the present time, an abundance of medication. But tonight, grateful was how I felt; grateful that the vet had indeed saved my life. The harsh reality was that without such intervention I surely wouldn't be here to tell the tale today.

So, I guess I had to admit, despite my current discomfort, these veterinary humans were miracle workers and had indeed saved some of my nine lives.

"No more grazing?" I heard Grandpa query in the distance. "What in the blazes is she talking about?"

"I have no idea," Countess Tiddles pondered with scepticism, "although I suspect we're in for some change."

Bambi ran into the kitchen to greet me with uncontrollable excitement, her fluffy tail bristling as she rubbed against me. Circling me, she sniffed,

"You smell odd Jack and you're all wobbly."

"The vets Bambi, that's what you can smell. I'm ok, really I am. Everything will be alright now," I encouraged reassuringly.

The few days ahead did indeed present challenges, not only for myself; the entire brood were subject to disarray and unwanted change.

For the remainder of the week Mummy confined me to the lounge during the evenings and she slept downstairs to ensure I wasn't left alone. My initial thought was that for some reason this was a punishment and I so desperately wanted to be upstairs with the others. Simba and Max would frequently awake me in the middle of the night, scratching desperately at the lounge door in attempt to gain entrance.

Why is Mummy doing this to me? What have I done wrong? I wondered sadly. Further clarification was provided when I eavesdropped a conversation between Mummy and Daddy.

"Has he used the litter tray yet?" Daddy asked on the second morning.

"He has," Mummy replied with a relieved sigh, "the vets will be pleased. You're a good boy aren't you Little Jack," She airlifted me for one of those cuddles.

So, it was for my own benefit I realised, that I was isolated during the evenings as Mummy and Daddy needed to monitor my urine output.

Throughout the course of the week I had regular checks at Crown House Vets; they left nothing amiss and I was subject to daily medication to help combat any infection.

The biggest challenge of all was mealtimes, which did provoke some upset within the brood; within no time we began to understand the meaning of 'grazing', or should I say the lack of. Upon reflection, we'd had it good for some time …we'd been accustomed to accessing an abundance of food whenever we wished.

Things had suddenly changed…and not for the better!

With all the scrumptious food suddenly withdrawn from me, I stood in protest when offered the bland, yukky stuff. Furthermore, it was with much mortification that I was confined alone during mealtimes. Disgruntled I stamped my paws and stomped in protest, hoping that Mummy would submit and resume my normal feeding regime once again.

This was not to be!

"He's just not tolerating the new food," Mummy complained to Clare the vet during one of my consultations, "One poo he's had in three days so he's obviously not eating enough."

I felt confidently smug that Clare, with all her fuss and cuddles, would surely fight my corner.

"Don't worry," Clare replied, "he will adjust. Maybe it's just a case of trialling different brands."

NOOOO! Clare, why are you doing this to me?

"He's on the low-fat range because, well, he is slightly overweight as you'll know Davina."

An embarrassed silence followed from Mummy.

So, Clare was calling me a 'fat ass' now! I grimaced.

I'd anticipated Clare to be slightly more of a 'push over' than the big man Jonathan, but no, she was as equally as adamant about my dietary needs.

Bloody rotten vets!

I listened in to the remainder of their conversation and conclusively it was with grave reluctance I had to admit these vets only had my best interests at heart. They really did. The putrid diet in question played an important role in helping to support my urinary tract. Effective management of my diet would minimise the risk of a further blockage by dissolving the crystals before they develop.

Tail between my legs, I had to accept the importance of the yukky stuff.

Mealtimes, once a pleasurable experience, proved to be something of a battle over the next few weeks which initially reduced Mummy into a stressed frenzy.

We took our usual positions in the kitchen the following morning; Magic, Max, Peanut, Pepper, Holly and Bambi would dominate the work surfaces.

Bad Boy Oliver lurked dangerously in the doorway then, with sudden gusto, ran and dodged the others to take his prime position near the microwave. Those who he couldn't pass by, he simply jumped over determinedly.

Jasper, Thor, Zena, Tiddles and myself swarmed Mummy's ankles and Treacle and Candy hovered impatiently upstairs.

Mummy began to prepare the food on the work surface. "Darren! Come and get Jack for his breakfast!" she bellowed.

"Here we go again!" I complained.

"Stop whining," grumbled Magic, his tummy rumbling, "at least you get fed first!"

Whispers of agreements filled the room whilst Oliver paced up and down impatiently!

"But you haven't tasted the stuff," I complained miserably before hearing Daddy approach.

"Come on little fella," Daddy picked me up...there was no way I was following him on this occasion, not with the pathetic food prescribed at present.

Confined to the lounge, I reluctantly nibbled at the humble offerings reluctantly that Daddy had given me. My tummy rumbling, I could just imagine the others devouring their succulent pouches and tasty biscuits as Mummy served them in the kitchen.

Despite the fact that Mummy was being her absolute best with discretion, my super sensory hearing recognised the sound of foil pouches being opened. I even heard Jasper purr while he feasted.

Miserably, I walked away from my food and sulked in a corner of the room.

"Hey! Don't be like that buddy!" Daddy pleaded.

"You try to eat it then!" I groaned despairingly. "You try eating this shite instead of your peppercorn steak, chicken, juicy beef and all your other succulent food, Daddy!"

"Mind your language, young lad!" Grandpa Jasper belched from the kitchen.

I scurried off up the stairs, disappointed in my parents, more so the brood. I lay on the bed reminiscing of how good things used to be; dreaming even as I slipped into a heavy sleep...

The humans would leave for that place called work and we would have the run of the household. As much as we loved our humans, having free reign over the home would maximise opportunities for some of us to embark on mischievous antics and sometimes cause a catalogue of disruption within or wake. Simba would happily claw and chew the furniture; Bambi, Zena and Holly would jump, leap, pounce on one another playfully after stampeding through the house, knocking ornaments over in the process. Max and Peanut would frequently sniff out where the Dreamies were hidden and had long since mastered opening drawers and doors; the packets included, devoured. I would confidently climb and claw my way up the curtains and swing proudly, unperturbed by the shredded state they were now in.

On the frequent occasions Simba would open the bathroom door, shredding and tearing at the toilet rolls provided much fun and satisfaction for me and when we'd exhausted all of our energies in doing the things we shouldn't be doing, we would resume playing with our toys and me, of course, my sparkly balls.

The more sensible of the brood; Thor, Magic, Tiddles, Jasper and Treacle would lazily potter around, enjoy extended siestas and eat throughout the course of the day.

Oliver would enjoy the solitude of his own room and showed little objection when we joined him, other than Simba of course, who frequently propelled him into a guarded hissing and spitting state.

This particular day was different however!

Upstairs, sprawled out on the bed, a frustrated roar disturbed my reminiscent sleep.

"Where the heck is the food?" Simba shouted.

Thor thudded along the hallway perplexed, then up the stairs, frantically in search, "My biscuits! Where are they?"

Tiddles virtually hoovered the floor in search of scraps, her gums providing perfect suction. Oliver and Simba ran around in a frenzied whirlwind whilst tiny Treacle ran frantically in search the missing bowls.

Magic stamped around irritably, muttering vulgarities beneath his breath.

It was Jasper who was most thwarted of all, he hoisted himself from the comfort of his bed and searched the house moodily for something, anything, to eat. "Where the blazes is the food? What in God's name is that woman playing at? It's just preposterous!" he muttered.

"It's HIS fault!" Simba accused officiously, glaring at me in dissatisfaction.

"Ain't on, this!" Oliver muttered, his expression sour. "I was given chicken on tap before all this absurdity."

"Now, now! The boy can't help it!" Magic defended.

And so, yes, meal times were certainly an ordeal over the following few days as Mummy and Daddy tried their best to encourage us to adapt to the new regime. Needless to say, several strategies were applied and this took numerous attempts.

Shutting me in a different room with either mummy or Daddy wasn't the best idea. I'd had enough isolation in my short life and this caused me far too much stress as I'd scratch at the kitchen doors to be fed amongst my peers. Bearing in mind I was also subject to three lots of medication daily which I detested.

"I know," Daddy suggested on the third day, "the others can have their food on the kitchen top. Jack can't climb up there. Feed Jack from the floor, then at least they're all together."

Treacle and Candy's feeding regime also continued as normal...they had always enjoyed their food from a great height in the bedroom, which I'd never been able to access anyway.

However, Daddy's suggestion was short lived. Despite the blandness of my diet, the others zoomed in curiously on the new dish, their predatory senses detecting something new on the menu, something different. Typical inquisitive felines; they wanted everything and anything they couldn't, or shouldn't, have.

Peanut would gulp at the putrid food greedily whilst Max would flick out what food he could with his paw.

Jasper, Magic and Simba jumped down and circled the bowl like piranhas.

Peanut, with his rapacious appetite, suddenly barged through and began to lick from the bowl.

"Hey, that stuff isn't for you!" I complained from the kitchen doorway, wishing I could access their food but the kitchen worktop was a height I'd never been able to master.

"Thought we shared," Peanut meowed, his nose coated in gravy.

"Think yourself lucky YOU'VE got decent food!" I muttered glumly and pivoted back into the lounge, still hungry.

At that precise moment Mummy appeared and shooed the others away, "C'mon guys! Away! That's Jack's food."

Strange creatures, us cats, always tempted by foods we weren't allowed, as repulsive as they may be.

As much as I had my humans wrapped around my ginger paws, I soon discovered my protests over the new diet were futile. The expensive but bland food was here to stay and within a short space of time, I readjusted to the change; hunger superseding my preferences.

Even with the new food regime in situ, with my free spirit, I never remained disheartened for long though;

"Little miracle you are Jack," Daddy murmured one night as I pawed on his knee, "where would we be without you, eh? My special boy."

"Um...our special boy." Mummy interjected.

"He always follows me."

"That's funny, I recall it being me who he follows."

I smiled to myself, knowing where the conversation was heading as the parents baited one another.

"If we ever separated I'd have full custody of Jack and you know it," Mummy continued.

"You stole him off me, getting him chipped in your name!" Daddy protested.

"He's my cat, that's why! And if it ever meant going to court, so be it!"

"Well, I'd have to have him at weekends then..."

I chuckled as the conversation continued; as much as they were enjoying their banter, the underlying threats were present. They both had an undeniable special love for me.

Blessed is how I felt, very blessed indeed.

It didn't take long for me to recover from my operation, the resilient chap I was!

The vet Jonathan who had operated on me, well, I appreciated now that I wouldn't be here other than for him. I owed him my life and the remainder of the veterinary team also who monitored me with such precision over the following days, weeks even.

Several weeks following my surgery a further event at the Rescue provided an opportunity for me to once again meet my Angel, Auntie Jill.

It was resident Toby's birthday and what better way than to celebrate it with a 'Resident Tea Party' event with an open house for the day with cakes galore!

Mummy made the decision to take Bambi, Holly and myself to the event. Holly after all, loved exploring the outdoor section of the chalets, experiencing the fresh air.

It was a wonderful event with an incredible show of supporters. Chirping from the confines of my chalet, I was eager to explore.

Holly was quite content absorbing everything that went on around her, drinking in the fresh air and watching the birds fly by with her predatory instincts. Bambi, somewhat overwhelmed, gravitated towards the rear of the chalet, the bustle and noise a tad overwhelming for her.

"It'll be fine Bambi. These are all good people, don't be scared," I encouraged but she was adamant to remain within the confines of her bed as she watched on with trepidation.

Bambi, a strange little character at times; she was exceptionally close to Mummy yet had become increasingly cautious around others. When friends visited the home she would often flee, taking comfort only from her human Mummy, so today wasn't perhaps her best experience.

Mummy, listening to my inquisitive chirping, placed me in a harness and allowed me to explore the grounds some.

I welcomed the fuss and attention provided, not in the slightest perturbed by an audience of supporters.

"Bloody typical! You get chosen again!" Holly wailed grudgingly from the chalet.

I weaved through the crowd ardently and welcomed the strokes and compliments from our supporters and volunteers alike, Mummy or Daddy keeping a tight grip on my reign throughout.

Volunteer Jill danced around me as she topped up the cake tiers. This had become her role for the day, it should have been Mummy but understandably any human with any level of intelligence simply knew how diabolical Mummy was with kitchen duties!

I stumbled into the furry boy himself, Toby, and curiously we sniffed one another.

"Long time, no see Little Jack," his gummy lisp came through load and clear, "how's things?"

"Good. Um…happy birthday Sir Toby. Have you had lots of treats?"

"What with scrum-didly-umptous chicken, toys, gifts and a knitted snake, one certainly can't complain. I say lad, you've gained some weight."

"I'm on a new diet regime due to a recent blockage. Food is utterly crap now," I grimaced, this morning's aftertaste still in my mouth.

"Don't even get me going on food! Bloody volunteers limit my treats these days. Worried about my weight they are with this diabetes."

"I know the feeling...but at least you're allowed chicken. Even that's forbidden for me now."

"You'll get used to it Jack, if it keeps us healthy I suppose we can't complain. Just irks me sometimes."

I knew the feeling only too well.

I bristled my tail as I could sense resident Harry nearby, unlike Toby he was a much more resilient chap. I scurried away hurriedly, dragging Mummy in tow.

True to her word my Auntie Jill and Lindon arrived, accompanied by the biggest cake ever for Toby's birthday celebration.

"Well then, you handsome boy," she smiled at me. Just look at you now; so big, strong and brave! You've certainly been through it, haven't you, eh?" it was more of a rhetorical question.

I welcomed her shower of affection and kindness and rejoiced in the hour spent with her company. She was, of course, intrigued to see Holly once more and indeed acquaint herself with Baby Bambi, but I, undoubtedly was her main source of attention.

I went home smiling that day, pleased to have met wonderful supporters yet again and certainly another reunion with my Auntie Jill.

My Angel.

The invasion of alien paws

Recuperated fully and somewhat readjusted to my new eating regime, I was once more invigorated and up to my cheeky antics with my rambunctious furry family.

'April Fools Day' though had another meaning at the Hanes household!

And this was certainly no joke!

Mummy arrived home unexpectedly early from the Rescue.

Our ears pricked and eyebrows were raised as she dropped her bags haphazardly in the hallway and rummaged around in the dining room.

"I've assembled the crate Davi!" Daddy shouted from the kitchen.

'The crate?" I turned to Holly who was beside me in the cat tree.

"Well, it can only mean only thing, can't it?" she replied.

"We've only just reclaimed that dining room!" Max complained, piqued.

"As long as it's not another bloody Oliver!" Simba grunted. "If it's babies then so be it, but surely not another one of him. I'll go on a hunger strike if it is, I tell you!"

"You! A hunger strike?" Magic dismounted the sofa as he spoke. "You can't go a morning without food with that voracious appetite, let alone a few days. I'm off to see what's going down."

With that, the feline inquisitor, prowled through the lounge to the hallway, his senses vigilant.

Curiously we followed. The cat carrier nearby the dining room door was swiftly taken into the dining by Mummy, but not before we could smell the stench of sickness, nor mistake the sound of babies crying.

I nudged Holly impatiently, "Well?"

"A mummy and babies it is. The mummy doesn't look too bad but the tiny kittens look disgusting, all wet and covered in faecal matter. Yuck!" she grimaced.

"Do you think they're poorly?"

"They don't look too well," Magic acknowledged with a sigh, "let's hope they're ok."

Mummy opened the door and shuffled past us and within moments she reappeared, armoured with cimicat, fleeces, syringes and a washbowl. This in itself indicated this litter would require some degree of additional human intervention.

"What do they look like?" Curiosity, as always, got the better of me.

"Grubby and smelly little things, that's for sure," Bambi said turning her nose up.

"Just remember how poor a state you were in!" Max admonished, sniffing the doorway of the dining room.

"I never looked like THAT! They look like rodents and smell like them too!" She turned her attention to me once more, "Pretty colours though Jack, little gingers and torties...if they make it, that is."

"That bad?" I frowned.

"Not looking promising lad, not in the slightest." Magic shook his head despairingly as he trotted back through to the lounge.

Later that evening, I overheard Mummy explaining to Daddy about the new mum and her poor babies;

"Lavender just seemed to have given up on them, so disinterested she was with them when I found her this morning at the Rescue. She's been fine prior to this. She doesn't look particularly well herself, thinking about it. The tiny ginger one was so dehydrated."

"Do you think they'll survive?"

"I don't know. I've bathed them, they have a heat pad and all are being supplemented. All I can do is try. I'll book them in at the vets first thing Monday," Mummy sighed.

So, the Mummy was Lavender and we'd now established that this litter required particular care and attention.

"Well I've been hand-reared too!" Bambi scoffed indignantly.

"Yeah...me too with the cimicat," Holly agreed.

"Most of us have," Thor intervened, "but these sound like they're struggling on a different level. Have a bit of compassion girls!"

The remainder of Mummy's weekend was absorbed as she fussed between the two litters; Luna and her polydactyls still vacated the upstairs. Lavender's litter, in particular consumed more time and mummy would frequently enter their room with a bathing bowl, something, which we'd never witnessed before.

"Why are they in such a state?" Daddy asked her.

"Lavender wasn't washing them and I've had to stimulate them after feeding, this helps to release their bowels and bladders. I must say, she's shown much more interest in them since being moved to a home environment. They're still very matted and the tiny one is struggling; he's putting up some fight though, God bless him."

"Sounds just like me!" Peanut exclaimed proudly, licking the remnants of my bowl greedily.

"Many of us have been hand reared by Mummy, myself included, who couldn't eat following emergency care at eight weeks old. This is something on a different scale, look at how much time she's spending with them," Max grimaced, "These are struggling."

"Not more?" Oliver's back bristled as he sniffed the dining room door. "The extra toes gang have already invaded the upstairs room...Now these! We're being taken over!"

"You were in that room for the very same reason, remember?" Grandpa Jasper confronted the street cat.

"Um…"

"Exactly! Then you just be quiet, young man! Just pray for these little ones, pray that they'll survive, because right now, their future is looking incredibly bleak."

With Grandpa Jaspers wise words, that's all we could do; pray for them.

Monday certainly involved a veterinary visit during which it was established, Mummy Lavender had a significantly high temperature and her toilet habits had also been a cause for concern. Vet Joe examined both Lavender and her babies thoroughly. I attended for my vaccination booster, aaawww Joe, I remembered vet Joe, the angel who had removed my eye ball all those months ago, alongside a further two balls they considered were surplus to requirement!

"I suggest bloods on Lavender, she doesn't look a well cat at all. Don't be too disappointed if none of these babies survive, they're all very anaemic and are weak." She continued to examine the most vulnerable of the litter, the fighting tiny ginger.

"He's dehydrated …we'll give him some fluids."

The same cycle continued for the following three days, during which the tiny ginger baby required additional fluids. Hand rearing didn't appear to be sufficient.

Lavenders preliminary bloods returned negative, which was somewhat of a relief for Mummy. The litter however and their demands upon Lavender, seemed to be draining her frail little body.

Whilst the polydactyl litter thrived upstairs, Mummy invested much additional time over the following weeks medicating, feeding and bathing Lavender's vulnerable babies, willing them to improve.

Slowly, but surely, as each week passed, signs of progress were evident.

"Tiny Tim's a fighter, that's for sure. Who would have thought he'd pull through," Mummy told Daddy as they approached their seven-week coming of age.

"Tiny Tim? Why's she given him a name?" I frowned, repositioning myself in our new sisal cat tree.

"You know what that means?" Holly teased. "She only names the ones she's keeping."

"Yeah! Such a give away! And he's pretty and ginger," Pepper added.

"Much cuter than you Jack, all fluffy with two eyes," Simba's malevolence was wasted on me.

"She can't!" I protested. "She just can't! She virtually signed an oath after adopting Oliver!"

Their tormenting comments evoked a significant amount of trepidation.

I dismounted the tree, as always, it took more than one attempt and twice as long as the others, due to the fact that my footing needed to be accurate. Mission accomplished, I pottered over to Grandpa Jasper who was snoring heavily.

I patted him gently several times to awake him.

Grumpily, he roused.

"It's siesta time, what on earth are you thinking of?" he yawned, disgruntled.

"It's important Grandpa," I urged and conveyed what the others had said.

"Oh preposterous! Take no notice, dear boy. Don't you understand, they're teasing you? Mark my word, Mummy was adamant there were to be no more after Oliver. Trust me."

"But he's ginger and fluffy...and she's given him a name!" I blurted.

"Absolutely nothing you need to concern yourself over, young man. And you surely know by now, our parents have a special love for you, nothing in the world could even compare to how they feel about you. You understand this, don't you Jack?"

"I do," I whispered.

The others continued to bait me some over Tiny Tim. I fell no victim however to their tormenting mischief. It was futile, after all, Granpda Jasper had reassured me this wasn't to be; the wise old man was categorically always right.

At eight weeks of age, the polydactyl babies, now hefty bundles of fluffiness, were ready to embark on their new journeys in life and explore new pastures. Mummy took them to the Rescue for rehoming alongside their Mummy, as always, she did so with a lump in her throat.

Lavender's babies were subsequently transferred to the freshly sanitised 'Maternity Pad' upstairs.

A few days following their transition, Mummy made an appointment at the vets for the kittens. Unfortunately for me, I had awoken with conjunctivitis and was subjected to sharing the journey to the vets with them.

Squawking and crying, their meows were piercing as I quietly sat in my carrier. I daresay Mummy's abysmal driving didn't console them any!

One of the tiny bundles of fluff paused and approached the edge of the carrier.

I sniffed; he sniffed.

"Who are you?" the miniscule voice whispered.

"I'm Jack. And yourself?" I asked hesitantly.

"Tim. Tiny Tim actually." Said the little voice.

Traitor! So, this was HIM! I grimaced, feeling an instantaneous stab of jealousy.

I sniffed again, the babies no longer smelt repugnant like they did all those weeks ago, and they smelt fresh even.

"When are you going back to the Rescue?" I blurted.

Silence.

"Well?"

"The Rescue? I don't know anything about a Rescue," he purred as another sibling cuddled into him, "Mummy's not said anything."

"She's not YOUR Mummy!" I gritted grudgingly. "She's MY Mummy and she's YOUR Foster Mummy. There's a difference. Do you understand?"

"You mean she's not my forever mummy?" the tiny voice whispered.

"No, she's not. When you're ready, you'll get sent to the Rescue and you'll have to live with another family. You'll all be split up and you'll go somewhere on your own."

I regretted the words the instant they left my lips.

I heard a little gasp...then silence.

Oh Jack! I condemned myself, this jealousy has turned you into a terrible beast.

I recoiled at my venomous words and the hurt I'd no doubt just inflicted.

"Um...what I actually mean...um...is that you'll find a wonderful family when you're well enough, and your new mummy will likewise take good care of you."

"But I've only ever known this Mummy," the small and tiny voice quivered, "I don't want another one. I thought this was my home."

Think judiciously how you word this Jack, you don't want to perpetrate any more hurt.

"I...um...well, you see Tiny Tim, our house is full...um...I'm part of a family of fifteen furries, some of which are big, enormous even, and ferocious. Um...with you being so tiny, well...um...Mummy would want you to go to a nice home, a less rambunctious home. You...um...really, well, you really wouldn't want to be part of our brood. There's Holly who's a witch; Bambi who's a spitfire; Simba who's salacious; Oliver who's a pugilist and we have a Grandpa who's evil and nasty, oh, the list goes on and on, Tiny Tim...Just look at my face, I'm living proof, this is what the precarious Peanut did..."

Slow down Jack! I thought, you're getting too caught up in such fabrications!

"Well, you wouldn't want that now, would you, Tiny Tim?"

"I thought after everything, I'd be staying. I guess if I make it, I'll have to get used to a new home," the little voice whispered and turned his attention to his siblings. He simply turned his back on me, wounded by my words.

The car suddenly ground to a halt and we were carried into the vets.

It was Ornella who we saw. She examined me first. The dye she inserted into my eye startled me some but I remained composed, the last thing I wanted was to took vulnerable and pathetic in front of Tiny Tim and his furry little invaders whilst they awaited their turn.

"Conjunctivitis," Ornella confirmed, "This is good, we have no ulceration or foreign body here. I will give you some medication. Hey Jack! I remember treating your precious brother...how is little Ooooliver, eh?"

I felt like saying he's still an antisocial swine, but thought better than to waste my meows.

I listened patiently as Mummy and Daddy sickeningly drivelled over tales of him to the vet, the pride in their voices unambiguous.

The babies were next on the table.

Ornella's voice raised a decimal or two as she lifted one of the fluffy bundles, "Aaaaaw! Tiny Tim! Just look at you now, eh! Loooook how you have grown, little boooooooy!". Her Argentinian drawl was always accentuated more so when she became excited over a cat.

She examined the babies thoroughly, their extended tummies in particular.

"Okay so results now confirm that Mummy Lavender is positive for Coronavirus, I'm afraid to tell you. This, here, I think we're looking at Coccidia, these are parasites in the babies' intestines. Yes, I'm sure of this. We will need samples then we'll start with medication." She latched on to the baby for longer than necessary. There was something about this Tiny Tim that heightened emotions in people…as long as he didn't get under Mummy's skin, which was my predominant concern.

"Lavender is going to the Rescue this week, she's already reserved," Mummy informed the vet. "I think she'll benefit from some reprieve from the babies. As well as she's done with them, she could do with some time spent recuperating. Once the babies are well enough, the little tabby baby here will be joining her in her forever home. I've potential homes for the two other females also."

I did my calculations, that still left two babies remaining, one being Tiny Tim. I frowned, something didn't quite seem right here.

The journey home was strained, however, I did the honourable thing by making conversation.

"I hope your tummies get better soon," I spoke to Tiny Tim with sincerity.

"Thank you. I hope your one eye gets better soon," the little voice whispered.

"Um...so that's good, eh, that some of you have a home already. That's really good. You'll get one soon too, along with your buddy there."

I could hear them purring as they spooned into one another.

"You think so?"

"Certainly, who could ever resist a ginger, eh? Our kind are very popular you know. It's usually the poor black and black and white cats that get 'left on the shelf'. What colour is your buddy there."

"I'm a ginger too but with exceptional tabby markings and I have big blue eyes...oh, and the name is Theo, by the way. ."

The kitten in question spoke buoyantly. Too buoyant for my liking, his tone oozed far too much impertinence and mischief.

I wasn't getting myself caught up in another debate, nor was I prepared to indulge in any more lies. It wasn't in my nature, oh heck! Mummy and Daddy would be so disappointed in me if they knew of this.

Lavender, true to Mummy's word, was taken to the Rescue for some much-needed recuperation. Did her babies fret for her? Not in the slightest! Despite the problem with their tummies, they continued to stampede around the Maternity Pad.

The thunderous noise of them chasing one another was constant.

"I wish they'd bloody well shut up!" Thor muttered, looking up at the ceiling, "Can't get any peace and quiet with them hurtling about."

"When are they going, anyway?" Simba frowned. "They seem to have been here for ages!"

"They need to get better." I replied.

"They'll be gone soon," Grandpa consoled. "They just need a little while longer for their tummies to mend. You needn't feel jealous, nor threatened Jack. Just have a little compassion for them, eh? You, of all furies, should be able to appreciate what it's like to feel unloved and poorly."

Sometimes, similarly to humans, we let our emotions overrule the stark realities and practicalities in life. Grandpa always put things into perspective, he always tried to make us see reasoning in any given situation. He always knew how to make one feel positive about oneself and likewise he had the ability to turn any negative situation into a positive one.

So, why did I worry so much?

Pawprints in abundance

I'd by now become accustomed to the noises that permeated from within the confines of "The Maternity Pad" and the vivacious play that could be heard was a definite indicator that the babies were on the mend.

I lay sprawled within the pod of my cat tree listening to the familiar sounds that resonated around me.

Grandpa Jasper's habitual snoring; Peanut's belching; Pepper's head butts; Thor's feminine cry when he sought attention; the sound of Simba skilfully opening doors; Holly and Max's bounding paws during play; Zena and Bambi's pawing and suckling; Magic and Treacle's vocal meows; Oliver's foul language, Mummy and Daddy's voices... and so on, each one of my family had their own unique characteristics.

I loved them all, each and every one of them. My precious brood had certainly helped shaped me in becoming the spirited and gentle soul that I was.

I smiled languorously; I loved my little world so very much.

I had a furry family who loved me unconditionally and human parents who adored me, of that I knew.

"I'm having a tattoo," Daddy informed Mummy.

"Oh yes?"

"Hhhmm, my favourite thing in the world," he pondered.

"What me?"

"No, Little Jack of course."

So, on the occasions Daddy was away from me, he still felt I was close as I sat engraved upon his arm.

Undeniably, life for me could have been so incredibly different, as Grandpa Jasper once said, despite my desperate situation all those months ago, I was one of the blessed ones, being in the right place at the right time.

Words could never quantify my love of life, the devotion I felt for my family and indeed the human friends I'd encountered along my journey.

"You just seem to touch hearts, little fella," Daddy would whisper to me often.

I didn't need my sight to reap the benefits of life, no, not at all.

I had all the riches I desired within my little world.

Not all were as fortunate as I, I thought dejectedly, there were still many out there abandoned, starving and in need of attention. As much as the Rescue continued to help many, it certainly wasn't in a position to help the entire over-populated strays. The stark reality was, that so many furries still desperately sought homes.

The litter currently occupying the Maternity Pad; would they have survived life on the streets, or their mummy for that matter?

I doubted so very much.

Tiny Tim, a sweet little character he was, and I'd long since asked for forgiveness for my unacceptable behaviour with him.

I wished him all the very best, all of them in their new homes. They were deserving of the best, just like me.

I fell asleep that night, cuddled with my Mummy, exulting in the security and love my family provided.

I could not, for a single moment, ever underestimate how fortunate and blessed I was.

"I SAID NO MORE DAVI!" Daddy exclaimed wrathfully, "ASOLUTELY NOT!"

"But..."

"NO! Oliver was the last, you know that! I said no more after Jack, didn't I? Then look what happened? Bambi! We couldn't even go to Tenerife without you pestering about her...waking up every morning in the apartment to hundreds of post-it notes saying 'BAMBI' plastered over the walls! Pathetic!" He paused for a deep breath.

"It's just..."

Mummy's attempt at getting a word in was futile as Daddy continued his exasperated speech.

"Then there was Oliver..."

"Now you can just stop right there! Would you, hands on heart, have let Oliver go?"

"He..."

"Tell the truth! Would you have been prepared to rehome Oliver?"

There was silence momentarily.

"I'm waiting!"

"Well, he was very needy..." Daddy's voice trailed off.

"They're all needy," Mummy objected.

"My final answer Davina is no! We're not discussing this again!"

Mummy shuffled into the kitchen, muttering to herself as she went, something she frequently did when she was peeved.

"I just knew she had a soft spot for that Tiny Tim, I knew it!" I blurted to Grandpa Jasper; my back bristled.

"I've told you, young man, there's no need to concern yourself over it. It simply won't happen, Daddy's adamant this time. She won't stand a chance."

"But he's beautiful and fluffy and ginger and his brother Theo ..."

"Jack, stop whining. There's no chance she'll pull this one off," Pepper said assuredly, "not at all. I'd even go as far as to bet one month of my Dreamie allowance."

"She's just being an opportunist."

"Trying it on, more like."

"There's absolutely no way daddy will say yes."

"And if Tim's so dependent upon his sibling Theo, they'll ideally need to be rehomed as a pair."

"If he's said no to one, then two's out of the question!"

The cascade of comments, from my furry friends was reassuring, to say the least.

"I think she's got a bloody nerve even asking!" Simba finally added icily, as always, he was zealous to have his opinion heard. Oliver skirted the perimeter of the room, eager to establish what was going on. It wasn't before too long he also viewed his opinion.

"I ain't having my chicken rations affected if any more arrive, I'm telling you! Bad enough when you had to change your diet Jack, affected us all, that did."

"Stop making the boy feel guilty, Oliver," Grandpa reproached. I gulped before being brave enough to pluck up the courage to defend myself. "Well, you ought to consider yourself lucky then, don't you, Master Oliver? You can still have chicken and given from your humble beginnings, you should be thankful you're not on any old cheap crap."

"Lad has a point," Simba acknowledged, momentarily distracted from chewing his claws in an effort to remove the outer sheath.

"I really don't know why this debate is taking place!" scolded Grandpa. "It's preposterous! Your ludicrous connotations Jack, are unsettling everyone. Please stop fussing and concerning yourself...I've never been wrong yet. Daddy simply will not allow this to happen."

But you see, I was concerned.

I went to bed that evening, snuggled against Mummy. She'd not really spoken to Daddy much following their last conversation, only in monosyllables, if that.

In itself, that was an indicator that Mummy was on a mission. Or was I over worrying?

As much as I loved my furry friends, I depended greatly on Mummy and Daddy and whilst they loved us all equally, they treated me with infinite affection and love, of course.

I knew what hardship, illness and pain were and I certainly felt wounded inside for the terrible start Tiny Tim and his siblings had suffered, I really did.

I wanted them to be well and to flourish...just not in my home! Sensing my unease, Candy jumped onto the bed and snuggled against me, honoured is how I should have felt, as she transiently abandoned her much loved Magic to tend to my needs.

"Right spill the beans! You're sulking Jack."

"It's nothing..."

"It is, c'mon," she prompted.

"It's just that he's ginger and cute and tiny and needy and pretty and fluffy. What if it happened? What if Mummy or daddy didn't love me the same, if they kept him?"

"First Jack; you should know by now they worship you, they're devoted to you and that will never, ever change. Secondly, Tiny Tim will not be staying. And even if he was, is it really such a big deal? Is it wrong to help another and let them grow and become cultivated within our family? Look at little Bambi and poor Oliver, look what we've all done for them! Not just Mummy and Daddy...US Jack! We've contributed towards their progress, all of us, as we did yours when you arrived. Have a restful sleep and awake more positive in the morning."

Candy's reassuring words eased my troubles some and she was right, I too, was provided the promise of a secure and loving future during my desperate time of need. Who was I to deprive others?

The litter in question still continued their frenetic escapades within the boundaries of the Maternity Pad for a further week.

They were now approaching eleven weeks of age; way beyond their expected rehome age.

Candy's words had indeed struck a chord and had provided me much time for positive reflection.

Should my philosophy be confirmed regarding Tiny Tim joining our family, then I would embrace him like I had the others. I would nurture him like I did so with the spitfire and I would show no malice or resentment.

Why?

Because the love I'd been provided had never lessened, despite new additions to our family in the past. Yes, Candy was right, Mummy and Daddy were dedicated to us all and from this I, we even, continued to thrive.

Mummy and Daddy didn't raise the subject of Tiny Tim again, not within earshot anyway. Despite my own predictions, the brood were relentless in their belief that Tiny Tim was to be rehomed elsewhere.

This indeed had been a complex litter in many ways and we had all become accustomed to listening to their noisy frolics within the confines of their room so it was with some astonishment that the persistent noise drew to a sudden halt one Saturday morning.

Aghast, we listened on assiduously.

The door squeaked open.

A cat carrier clanged and copious purrs and meows could be heard as Mummy dismounted the stairs clumsily.

"Darren, I'm off!" she shouted from nearby the front door.

"Are you taking them all today?"

"I am."

"Well I'll be busy working on the new catio, Dave's coming to help. Don't be late home from the Rescue, will you?"

"I won't."

And with that, she was gone. Simply gone with Tiny Tim and his siblings in tow.

"Ha! All that worry over nothing Jack, we all told you he'd be going!" Simba mocked.

The brood giggled, jested and taunted me intermittently throughout the course of day. Even Grandpa Jasper made reference to the situation.

"See, dear boy, I told you this Tim wouldn't be staying. I'm never far wrong."

They clearly thought my naivety was amusing. I slumped on the sofa despairingly.

Once the jokes had abated some, the furries drew their attention to the catio Daddy was building for them outdoors.

They watched on in awe as the large open-air structure was finally taking shape.

"Oh Jack! This will be amazing for us!" Holly exclaimed in delight, "I heard Mummy telling Daddy we will be having a little Zen garden with non-toxic plants and a water feature. We'll have outdoor cat furniture and we'll be able to watch the birds, the bees and the butterflies. Don't worry Jack, we'll describe what they look like for you."

"And you can enjoy the fresh air and listen to all the new sounds, little fella," Magic smiled.

"It'll be fabulous!" Max exclaimed, "I haven't caught a fly in ages, there'll be loads out there for me."

"Spiders are more my kinda thing," Tiddles pondered.

"Anything for me," Oliver intervened, "as long as I can put into practice my amazing hunting skills."

"Oh, I simply can't wait to feel that sunshine on my back!" Zena sighed.

"Well, if food out there is part of the deal, then I'm in!" Peanut, as always, put his rapaciousness love of food, first and foremost.

"I'll be able to sprawl in the sunshine all day long!" Thor sighed languorously.

"At last! I'll finally be able to wind up the dog from next door," Simba said, "if he thinks us teasing him from the window is bad enough now; wait till we get out there, he won't know what's hit him!"

The others were evidently excited over this new outside living area that Daddy was constructing.

Disinterested with talk of the catio, my thoughts were with Tiny Tim. I had deep regrets over my jealousy of him and how I must have made him feel during our journey to the vets that day. Where would he go? What would become of him? So tiny and vulnerable, he was.

Feeling somewhat hollow for the remainder of the day, I couldn't wait for Mummy to return home from the Rescue. A cuddle was all I wanted right now, a human cuddle.

After was seemed like an eternity, a key turned.

The door opened.

Mummy entered the hallway, empty cat carrier in tow. We'd learned by now this was normality once she had taken a litter for rehome.

Simba suddenly jolted upright, his back bristled, his predatory eyes widened as he sniffed.

"What the bloody hell...?" Simba shrieked, enraged.

I gasped!

Sharp intakes of breath resonated from around me.

The furry clan, all fourteen of them, then drew to a sudden standstill.
A palpable silence fell upon the house.

A high-pitched squeak from Tiny Tim... a piercing shrill broke the tense stillness.

"HI EVERYBODY! I'M HOME FOR GOOD!... and guess what? My brother Theo is staying for keeps t o o!"
An excited "YIPEE!" followed from the two tiny invaders.

Twenty-nine eyes glared at Mummy disbelievingly, accompanied with a simultaneous and incredulous wail, "OH! MUMMY....NOT AGAIN!"

Little Jack's Special Moments

Little Jack & Holly

Little Jack with Mummy & Daddy

And Finally – Meet all Little Jack's Friends

Mr Magic Hanes

Grandpa Jasper

Countess Tiddles, the Fangless Wonder

Simba the Destroyer

Tiny Treacle

Princess Pepper

Little Miss Candy

Little Man Max

Teddy Bear Thor

Princess Zena

Baby Peanut

Baby Holly

Master Oliver Hanes

Baby Bambi

Tiny Tim

<u>**Baby Theo**</u>

Acknowledgements:

My heartfelt gratitude extends to all those who have continued to support, love and care for Little Jack throughout his remarkable journey so far.

The love we have for this special boy simply cannot be quantified in words, he is an immense part of our lives: every day bringing smiles, laughter and love.

Without Oldham Cats Rescue, Little Jack's fate most certainly could have been different and I'm honoured to be part of a registered charity, which puts the welfare of cats first and foremost.

A sincere thank you to all of the team at Crown House Veterinary Practice who have unquestionably extended some of Little Jack's 'nine lives' on more than one occasion. Little Jack has certainly faced challenges in terms of his health and during such worrying times, the veterinary care he's received has been exceptional throughout.

An immense thank you goes to the supporters of Oldham Cats Rescue who also play a pivotal role in the success of the Rescue: As a non-profit charity with no funding, our Rescue survives purely from the good will of the public.

Little Jack has certainly gained some amazing supporters along the way, in particular Oldham Cats Rescue Facebook members, who have demonstrated an unprecedented fondness and love for him. I want to thank you all for your continued support, love and care and contributions to the Rescue. Little Jack's followers have certainly inspired me to write this sequel.

My dear friend, Lucy Cobb, I cannot express enough my gratitude for the way in which you have supported Oldham Cats through your own fundraising and for being there for Little Jack and our other furries at the Rescue. Through Little Jack, I have gained a true fiend and Jack has indeed gained another angel.

Auntie Jill Murfin, I believe in Jack's short life so far, he's had many an angel watch over him but you are truly an exceptional angel. Your love for this special furry is undeniably unprecedented, through which I'm very blessed to have gained another dear friend.

It's with enormity I thank Darren, my husband, who has supported me throughout my rescue work and who equally invests so much love, time and care into our furbaby family. The words, "No more Davina!" were said three cats ago, but eventually, he also, fell victim to certain incredible little characters: their vulnerabilities and personalities leaving paw prints on his heart.

My daughters, Chanel and Cerys, it's not always easy having a 'crazy cat lady' for a mum and sometimes sacrifices have had to be made and plans cancelled when there have been cats or kittens in need, I thank you both for your love, support, inspiration and empathy.

My publisher Lionel Ross, your support, reassurance and encouragement have played an integral part during this publication, and have contributed to my fortitude and confidence when writing this book.

It's with much gratitude I would like to mention my fellow trustees and volunteers of Oldham Cats Rescue: all of you have supported Little Jack along his journey and your belief in me has inspired me to write this book.

Faye Kennerley, my treasured friend, thank you perpetually for supporting me through some difficult moments whilst writing this book: for always being there for me and always having faith in me.

Dear friend, Patsy Cahill, your time and superlative hours spent assisting in the proof reading of this book has been valued and greatly appreciated: I thank you immensely.

Karl Whitehead
(Photography by Karl / www.photographybykarl.co.uk) thank you eternally for the use of your beautiful photos of Little Jack and Holly, taken at your studio.

A heartfelt thank you to all those who have been so very generous, enough to sponsor the publication of this book, all proceeds will certainly go to Oldham Cats Rescue to help care for, feed and medicate many more of our feline friends who cross our gates:

Crown House Veterinary Surgery: (50 – 54 Milnrow Road, Rochdale, OL16 1UD, United Kingdom)
Email: info@crownhousevets.co.uk. Telephone: 01706 646815/ 01706 357796/ Fax: 01706 357796:

Lucy Cobb – Uppermill Ladies Fashion Boutique (33 High Street, Uppermill, Saddleworth, OL3 6HS/ 01457875975/ info@lucycobb.com / www.lucycobb.com):

Susan Darwin Photography – 0161 792 8988.Susan Darwin Photography,https://www.facebook.com/ Susan-Darwin-

244

Photography-1030780693627425/.
(susandarwinphoto@btopenworld.com):

Jill Murfin; Darren Metcalfe and John Anthony Hampson; John Norman and Jennie; Faye Kennerley, Samantha Fahmy; Bev Young and David Wesley; Tricia Boulding and Chris Boulding; Sharon Harrington, in memory of her much-loved fur baby Cass, who is never forgotten; from Little Jack's furry fan club... fur babies Merlin and Abbie; Joan Longworth; Ann Roddy; Kci Severs; Jay Gansler and James Gansler and Lesley McNeil.

Finally...and last but not least, one enormous thank you to Little Jack himself. You have inspired me throughout whilst writing this sequel to 'The Life of little Jack'.
One would never have imagined, all those months ago, when you were rescued from the streets, that you would have changed our lives, touched our hearts, made us laugh and made us cry, even.

An unquantifiable love we have for you Little Jack, you're unique and beautiful in every way and certainly have left paw prints on many a heart.

We love you, Lion Heart.